A 682

SPUR PUBLICATIONS
POULTRY FANCIERS' LIBRARY

General Editors:
DR. J. BATTY   MRS. M. BATTY

BANTAMS FOR EVERYONE

OTHER BOOKS AVAILABLE

Understanding Old English Game—Large and Bantams
Dr. J. Batty

Royal Pastime of Cockfighting
Robert Howlett
(Reprint of 1709 classic)

Managing Poultry for Exhibition
H. Easom Smith

Bantams and Miniature Fowl
W. H. Silk
(Second Edition)

Ornamental Water Fowl
A. A. Johnson and W. H. Payn
(Third Edition)

History of Cockfighting
G. Ryley Scott

1. Rosecomb, Black Male
2. Japanese, Black-tailed White Male
3. Barbus d'Uccles, Millefleurs Female
4. Frizzle, White Female

BANTAMS

5. Sebright, Silver Male
6. Barbus d'Anvers, Blue Male
7. Modern Game, Black-red Male
8. Modern Game, Pile Female

BANTAMS
for everyone

H. Easom Smith

Past President of the Poultry Club

Author of:
Modern Poultry Development
Managing Poultry for Exhibition

Saiga Publishing Co; Ltd
Hindhead, Surrey

Second edition February 1976
Reprinted November 1976

© H. Easom Smith, 1976

Reprinted 1979

ISBN 0 904558 11 8

Reproduced, printed and bound in Great Britain
at The Pitman Press, Bath

SAIGA PUBLISHING CO; LTD
1 Royal Parade, Hindhead, Surrey, England, GU26 6TD

CONTENTS

PREFACE TO SECOND EDITION

In more than fifty years of reading poultry literature I have never come across a book about bantams which was both truly objective and free from personal bias. Most writers drew only on their own experiences and formed them into methods to serve as a pattern which, they thought, would necessarily bring success to all. Not seeking to justify what they wrote, they offered vehement opinions in place of facts.

This did not preclude some guidance being offered; but over-enthusiasm on the part of the writer stifled thought and imagination by the reader. The big letter 'I' freely used does not often betoken a balanced approach to a subject.

It was with these thoughts in mind that I drafted the first edition of this book. My intention was to set down what is known about bantams in some coherent order so that much of the book would apply to all breeds kept by bantam fanciers in all places at all times.

What it offered was more than the result of personal experience. It was also a concensus of views of breeders whom I have known for a great number of years and with whom aspects of bantam breeding have been discussed on many occasions. I tried hard to be objective.

That part of the book which relates to management and breeding gave instruction on standard practice. By modifying equipment to suit accommodation and the particular needs of any breed the basic principles can be applied everywhere and will bring success.

When each breed is briefly described in Chapter 16 I allowed myself the luxury of adding little bits of personal opinion—but with this difference. My opinions are unbiassed and based on careful observation of the breeds as seen at the major shows and as they have passed through my hands when judging. With the exceptions of two of the minor breeds mentioned on pages 161–62 I have judged all the other sorts, at one time or another.

For the first time, I believe, authenticated egg-laying records of bantams are set down in a book. These may be at variance with figures quoted by enthusiasts of some of the laying breeds but facts are stubborn things and must receive more careful attention than opinions.

It will be noted that this book does not contain a chapter on ailments and diseases. It is my view that veterinary medicine is now so advanced and new diseases likely to be so severe, that much home-doctoring would be both misdirected and ineffective. Minor troubles which occur occasionally receive brief reference, with suggested treatment, in Chapter 18. This also includes notes on terms in common use which formerly comprised that 'sacred cow' of poultry manuals, the Glossary of Terms.

My aim was to write a book which could be regarded as the textbook on the subject of bantams, most likely to help the newcomer and not without interest for the experienced breeder. Those who wish to get fullest value from what they read will use *British Poultry Standards* in conjunction with this work.

When I wrote this introduction I learned from the secretary of The Poultry Club which incorporates the British Bantam Association, that more than one hundred new members had been enrolled during the year I was President of that body.

This, surely indicated a move towards the simpler, lovelier things of life as exemplified by the homely but interesting and skilful business of breeding and preparing bantams for show.

Now that the pith of more-than-a-million words which I contributed to POULTRY WORLD committed to the pages of this guide to bantam keeping have been revised, I hope that it will still be found to be reliable and trustworthy.

Gatherley Castle, Brompton on Swale, 1975.   H.E.S.

Chapter One

BANTAMS—SHOW POULTRY OF TODAY

What is a bantam? It is either a naturally dwarf form of domestic fowl or a miniature, to represent a large breed, which has been created by skilful poultry breeders.

A bantam is the pre-eminent show fowl of today. It is bred in thousands where once it existed in hundreds. Many of today's breeders have never owned large poultry and think only of bantams when they think of poultry shows.

When regard is given to the economic conditions of this second half of the twentieth century and the lack of land available to any except the richest, the reasons for the success of the bantam as the means to satisfy a yearning for show poultry become apparent.

Shows still offer the same scale of prize money as they did before the 1939 war. The main incentive to showing is to gain honours and these are as open to bantams as to large poultry.

Prices for surplus stock are not substantially different and the main reason for bantams changing hands is, again, to enable someone else interested in the honours of showing to obtain stock of sufficiently high quality.

These two factors, taken together, mean that the rewards are not vast, even when a breeder is highly successful at both showing and producing the right sort of stock.

On the other hand, everything connected with the hobby or business of bantam breeding has—as they now say—escalated. Feeding costs have increased to a very large extent. Transport to shows, whether by rail or road, are higher than at any other point in time. Hampers, pens and other *impedimenta* necessary to showing are all much dearer.

It is, therefore, necessary to cut down the costs of the production side of show poultry to make a better balance between expenditure and income. This can be done by breeding and exhibiting bantams because they offer certain natural advantages.

Being smaller in body they need less food than do large poultry. They are lighter in weight and need smaller pens, smaller baskets, smaller houses. All these are relatively cheaper.

Yet the rewards are immediately comparable. A bantam can win a first prize of the same value as any other fowl. It is eligible for the 'plums' of the exhibition world, and frequently wins them by being selected for honours such as best bird in show.

It offers a wider variety because there are both the miniatures of existing large breeds and the natural dwarfs which have no large counterparts. This means that the classification ought to be more extensive for bantams at any modern poultry show—and this is the case. The opportunities for winning prizes with bantams are that much wider because of the greater number of classes.

Bantams offer a greater diversity of form and colour than any other small, domestic livestock. No matter whether one looks for something sedate enough to walk about the lawn or hardy enough to roost in natural woodland, it can be found amongst bantam breeds.

All of them have the ability to pay for some part of their keep by virtue of the fact that all their products are edible. Eggs which are not needed for hatching or are, in the case of the newer breeds of miniatures, laid out of the normal rearing season may be sold to be eaten. Surplus birds of both sexes make delectable small chickens with a full, natural flavour. Many breeds make ideal broody hens in season and find a market for this purpose, among estate owners and game-keepers.

The triple points of eggs, meat and potential hatchers and rearers can be combined in some breeds and they are in big demand for these reasons.

Bantams have many advantages and few disadvantages. They have more classes at shows than any other form of present-day poultry. They have mass appeal, especially when the owner wants something which is intended to 'bring the garden to life' and finds that peacocks are both expensive and destructive.

They are useful—and this is a thought which many young parents may find acceptable—as a first means of bringing to the notice of a child those basic facts of life which it must encounter with advancing age. Nothing could be more appealing than the day-old, fluffy bantam chick. The explanation of how it came into being is capable of being handled in a straightforward manner which has the ring of truth and decorum.

Nothing could be more appealing than the day-old chick; nor, to the bantam man, the bantam which develops from it. In many forms and colours it is the show fowl of today.

Those with a taste for experimental breeding will find the same economies that belong to bantams for exhibition. Their housing and feeding costs will be less and more birds can be reared, for a given sum. By following some pre-planned system of breeding, principles of genetics can be proved as well with bantams as any other form of small livestock.

There might be interest for some people in creating, in bantam form, some of those old-time exhibition breeds of poultry which have been missing from the showbench for some time.

Whatever their wish in the realm of poultry breeding—with the exception of mass production of eggs or table poultry—bantams will completely fulfil requirements.

Chapter Two

HISTORY OF DEVELOPMENT

Bantams have come right from the back rank to the front in a life-time. Although they have been known for nearly two hundred years, development was not rapid until some forty years ago.

Before that, almost every book which referred to them, dismissed bantams as 'small fowls from Java' from the place named Bantam—and left it at that. It was, of course, common practice in the early days of poultry breeding to name breeds after their point of origin. If, therefore, there had been some small breed shipped from Bantam it would be natural for it to be so named.

The fact remains that no one breed has ever been traced as the original from which all others sprang. It is worth passing notice that the 'Bantam from Java' theory seems to have been commonly accepted because the breed which we know as the Black Rosecomb is called 'Java' at Continental shows.

Admitting that small works of high artistic merit have originated in Japan and China (e.g. Bonsai or dwarfed trees) and that it is more than likely that trading sea captains brought birds from the Far East in the past, the fact remains that some sort of native dwarf fowl appears to have been known from the earliest days when poultry breeding was taken seriously and books were written about it.

A famous author of his day, Harrison Weir, published a drawing of 'Old bantams, 1801' which were much like the bantam known as Booted. They were, perhaps, somewhat coarser but had single combs and feathered legs which made them readily recognisable.

He lists, as existing in 1810, bantam breeds with these names: English Dwarf, white in colour and of a size said to be equal to a

Some early Game and White Bantams, the latter afterwards known as Rosecombs

(*Taken from colour plate following p. 248 'The Poultry Book' by W. B. Tegetmeier*)

'middling sized pigeon'; Chinese Dwarf, shown as with heavily feathered shanks, buff in colour (These could well be considered the forerunner of Buff Pekins, which were to come into England from China as a distinct breed). French Dwarf, described as not being as small as the English breed; and Java, later to be the Rosecomb.

In 1842, Bonington Moubray depicted the Sebright and made some reference to it being originated by the baronet whose name it bears. He also mentioned a South American variety being 'partridge spotted and streaked'. In view of his observations on various breeds of large poultry it would appear that Moubray was not keenly interested in bantams and tended to dismiss them without much research into the breeds already known.

By the time his work was published, Britain was already a fairly open book to those who had travelled by the then expanding railway network. Had he wished to enquire closely there is no doubt that Moubray could have done so.

A serious work, *The Poultry Book* by W. B. Tegetmeier, did set out to describe bantams of the day. He described and named some which were destined to be the foundation material on which today's developments were based. It says much for the skill of the original breeders that some of them have lasted so well especially those which cannot gain points from other breeds and must have been inbred for upwards of a century.

Tegetmeier's list included White Booted; Black-red Game (neither Modern nor Old English names were then used); Sebrights; Black and White Bantams (not yet named Rosecombs); Pekin or Cochin; Japanese; Frizzled feathered from Japan; Nankin, so called because they were the colour of nankeen cloth; Creepers or Jumpers, probably the forerunners of Scots Dumpies; Fly-fishers, closely approaching the Blue-dun Game and 'others named from the marks on their feathers as in the Spangled and Partridge bantams'.

It is open to conjecture whether this latter group were the 'bantams of the countryside' from which Old English Game are variously alleged to have sprung.

In a later mention of Game, this author names Brown-red, Duckwing and Pile. These, together with the Black-reds he first portrays, were the basic material which was developed into the breed now known as Modern Game.

At this point the list consisted of two sorts of bantams. Those which were, more or less, native to Britain formed one group. They were not highly developed. Those which were imported from the East formed the second group and their characteristics appear to have been more firmly fixed. The outstanding exception was the Sebright, man-made to a pattern in England and developing rapidly.

Progress was, more or less, halted until the late 1890's. Even that masterpiece of poultry literature, *The Book of Poultry* by Lewis Wright could only give 30 out of 591 pages to bantams. His list was more selective than those mentioned above. He was not sidetracked into mentioning every dwarf which came his way and appears to have concentrated on those seen at the larger shows.

Black and White Rosecombs (now known by the present name); Sebrights; Black Pekins; Rumpless; Game; Black-tailed white Japanese; Cuckoo (near Dumpies but later to become Scots Greys); Booted; Nankin and 'Russian' bantams are all mentioned.

Of this list only the 'Russians' have fallen by the wayside. The rest are with us today.

The year 1893 marked an important step forward for bantams. In this year L. C. Verrey wrote the *Book on Bantams* said to be the first devoted solely to their breeding and culture. Points of interest were that Game were still not divided into Modern and Old English; Malays are mentioned as are Sultans and the beginning of Indian Game. This was followed, a year later, by *Bantams* by W. F. Entwistle. This book included standards for all breeds then known, which were afterwards embodied in the Poultry Club Standards of 1901. Otherwise indications are similar to another of Wright's books which seems to have accepted the fact that the small breeds had come to stay and were making a pretty good job of it, too.

The Practical Poultry Keeper, 1899, says that W. F. Entwisle had re-produced in bantam form almost all large breeds of poultry. This is the first clear indication of 'bantamisation' as understood today as opposed to the casual crossing of any existing bantam breeds to see what might result.

In addition Lewis Wright attributed to Entwisle the dictum that bantams which were miniatures of large breeds should be one-fifth the weight of their large counterparts. This is the rule which has been accepted from that day to this.

The list shown in this book included Malays, Aseels, Andalusians, Leghorns, Hamburghs, Polands, Spanish, Dark and Light Brahmas, Houdans, Silver grey Dorkings, and Sultans and Silkies. It is, of course, open to doubt whether the two last named should have been included. Although fairly small in stature they have long been classified as large fowl, light breeds.

In 1902 another great writer of his day, Harrison Weir, asked for two divisions to be created, one for pigmies which are miniatures of large breeds and the other for true bantams. He also mentioned, for the first time, Old English Game bantams and described the 'White Frizzled new bantam hen' which was drawn with a topknot.

At this point it is as well to take stock. Up to 1902 reliance has had to be placed on such facts as writers knew at the time they published their books. They may have acted in good faith but had, necessarily, to rely for a good deal of their material on breeders and exhibitors. They, in turn, were quite outnumbered by those who favoured large poultry which, at the turn of the century, could yield a man a comfortable living as long as his birds had larger size or brighter feathers than those of his rivals.

Shortly afterwards modern poultry journalism started with weekly papers which carried notes on breeding, reports of winners at shows, and advertisements of stock for sale. I have had access to the files of bound volumes of POULTRY WORLD and from this point in the history of bantams, statements can be verified.

The great show of the year was the Crystal Palace, later to be the Grand International Show. Taking it as a yardstick it may reasonably be concluded that this was the biggest classification likely to be offered for bantams in the course of the year. All other shows would be lesser in extent.

At the 1907 Crystal Palace show there were classes for: Malays; Modern Game; Indian Game; Sebrights; Brahmas; Rosecombs; Pekins; Japanese; Polands; Booted; Scots Greys; Buff Rocks; Frizzles; Wyandottes (Partridge, Silver-Pencilled and A.O.C.); and Any Other Variety (A.O.V.), in which the chief winners were Black Spanish, and Silver-Spangled Hamburghs.

Until the outbreak of the 1914–18 war the position was pretty much the same. There were no great developments and many of the breeds which Entwisle was said to have originated had, for all practical purposes, died out.

Some small breeders had come to the fore by breeding winners which bigger men gladly bought from them. During this period there were many articles of instruction in the pages of POULTRY WORLD but the same breeds were usually dominant. Shows were giving just a few more classes for bantams by this time but large fowl still held the centre of the stage.

The 1914–18 period was important because poultry took on a new importance. People realised, in the stringent days of rationing, the need to produce what food they could in their backyards and some chose bantams as a means to this end.

On 20th July 1917 there was, for the first time as far as can readily be traced, an account of bantams for utility. True, this referred to getting Old English Game to maturity at 17 weeks of age, by selection; but the word was used. Utility was soon to take on a new meaning.

In the weekly journals photographs were now used in place of drawings and assessment of progress became more readily possible. Reports gave details of items of interest and, if they could all be culled, would trace the history of most of today's breeds.

Kendal, which had previously been a Game specialist show, had classes for Variety bantams in 1920 and Light Sussex were classified, for the first time ever.

One of the classic shows, Birmingham, gave a comprehensive classification in the same year. For the record there were classes for Old English Game; Modern Game; Sebrights; Pekins; Japanese; Plymouth Rocks; Hamburghs; Rosecombs; Wyandottes; Frizzles; Scots Greys; Brahmas; Indian Game and A.O.V. in which winners were White Polands, Millefleur Belgians and Light Sussex.

Possibly as a result of post-war influences there was a new surge of interest. This was recognised by the amendment by H. Inman of a work previously published from the pen of P. Proud. Revised in 1924 this small book mentioned, in addition to those shown at Birmingham: Modern Game in White, Blue, Blue-red and Lemon-blue; Buff Orpingtons; Minorcas; Columbian and Buff Columbian Wyandottes; Belgians; Yokohamas; Sumatras; Anconas; Black Orpingtons; Langshans; Faverolles and Rhode Island Reds in their early days.

This was the state of the market for the next fifteen years. A few breeds were brought forward; a few lost ground. Substantially the material available was the same. But there were changes in organisation. Changes in attitude towards bantams. Changes in support. And changes in the attitude of *judges* towards bantams.

In 1933 was announced the formation of The British Bantam Association. It was organised on a territorial basis and many of the leading bantam breeders gave it immediate support. This body was formed to promote bantams as the showbird of the future and how true was the vision of founder members.

In addition to providing special prizes and specialist bantam judges, it planned for a big club show each year in addition to the three classics which then obtained. For a too brief time this was a golden era.

Its end was, ominously enough, foreshadowed by a blaze. On the last day of November 1936 the Crystal Palace was burned down and all the records of the International Poultry Show were lost.

In 1937, on July 16th, The Poultry Club announced the formation of a Judges Board of which the first chairman was Mr. R. S. Walters, then secretary of the Birmingham Fat Stock Show. Centenaries of the older agricultural societies fell about this time. That of the Great Yorkshire Society was at York in 1937.

News items of interest began to centre on the remaking of some of those old, lost varieties which had never become firmly established. Amongst them, the Partridge Pekin. Still in 1937 it is noteworthy that a Welsummer was placed in the Any Other Variety class at the Dairy Show.

Two more years in this strain and then that fire in the sky caused by the Crystal Palace was reflected a thousand times more when bombs and fire rained down on Britain in the grimmest struggle of all time.

Between 1939 and 1945 food of any sort was at a premium and bantam keepers had to eke out rations as best they could. The 'kitchen scrap and balancer meal' era was in with a vengeance.

Those who could, kept their studs of bantams, although in much lesser numbers. Egg production had to have preference and larger birds, of less perfect Standard points, were often preferred to those of more perfect markings and neater size.

When, for the first time for several years, we slept peacefully through an undisturbed night again and gently flexed our muscles preparatory to taking up the threads of our old life, we found that the nucleus of many important breeds had been maintained.

Seeing the need for something to take the place of the old Crystal Palace Show and for some focal point of interest for breeders of Standard poultry, the journal POULTRY WORLD and the group with which it is connected, promoted the National Show in 1945. It was an instant success. It caught the imagination and filled the need of the day. For the purposes of this book it is worthy of record that a Spangled Old English Game bantam hen took the Poultry Club Trophy at this show—a sign of the times and the future.

Soon outgrowing the Horticultural Hall, the event was taken to Olympia where it became not only a show but an exhibition and the trade fair of the poultry industry.

Bantams now outnumber large fowl at all shows where a normally comprehensive classification is offered. The birds themselves are of good quality, having recovered from being bred oversized for egg laying during the war years. At the same time those days have left their legacy—and not a bad one, at that. Bantams are now of sufficient size and health to win, lay, live and reproduce their kind. The days when bantams were 'dwarf fowls from Bantam, a place in Java' have gone—for ever. In their place are such modern breeds as Marans, Faverolles, Minorcas, Welsummers and Sussex, so selectively bred that they not only win prizes but lay eggs which win their classes, too.

Chapter Three

BUYING FOUNDATION STOCK

Anyone really interested in bantams will wish to own home-bred stock. There is little pleasure in buying birds either for showing or laying purposes.

No sense of purpose will be achieved by merely purchasing bantams which have won prizes, unless they all come from one source and are also recommended by their breeder as suitable for breeding.

There are several ways in which foundation stock can be got together. They are effective in direct ratio to the amount of thought and money which will be spent. Not that a very deep pocket is wanted to buy good breeding bantams but, it is obvious, rubbish at the lowest price can never breed birds of the highest quality. As in most other interests, good stock costs reasonable money.

Hackneyed advice is that those wishing to make a start should write to the breeder of their choice—after his bantams have been seen winning at shows or he has been recommended from some reputable source or noted from an advertisement—and state clearly that they are inexperienced and wish to make a proper start in the selected variety. This is hackneyed only because it is the best advice that can be given and worth repeating.

There are four basic ways in which a start can be made. All of them have been used on innumerable occasions and all have yielded some measure of success.

Method 1, is most highly recommended and the slight extra initial outlay is thoroughly justified. A basic breeding pen consists of one male and two females. Bantams are usually sold in trios, in this manner. The idea is that fertility will be better and the flow of eggs from two layers will enable a 'sitting' (a number of eggs for hatching together) to be gathered more readily in season.

Under this method a trio is obtained from the breeder of choice. He will have balanced the pen so that age marries with youth and good points are balanced with bad. No one stud can claim a monopoly of the virtues and there are bound to be some slight deficiencies somewhere. It may reasonably be expected that, a fair price having been paid, good value will be received and the trio will breed something near the mark for exhibition purposes.

On advice or from observation, another stud is also selected because the bantams from it are strong in some point where the first choice is weak. Thus, the first choice may yield a trio with slight white in earlobes which are otherwise red. The second stud has bantams which are excellent in lobe colour.

From the second stud one really good hen is bought. She is added to the breeding pen and chicks are reared from her. They should be marked, when hatched, so that they can be known.

If the first stud is A and the second B there will be a number of pure A chicks and some which are AB at maturity. The latter group should be better in lobe than the pure A strain and a cockerel could be selected to head a breeding pen in the following season. Offspring from this pen would be from an AB male to AA females $= A_3 B_1$.

An alternative would be to use an A male to AB females or to have a pen of pure A stock. Or two chances may be had with two pens.

The big advantage of bringing in a strange female in the initial stages is that it can be blended into the whole of the stock, if successful in breeding the points desired, or rejected in the early stages if success is not achieved. There is no secondary outlay for new stock, either. All investment made in the first year should yield a dividend.

Method 2, is to buy one breeding trio from one source. As it is unlikely that any breeder would release stock equal to the best of that he retains, the time is hardly ripe for the new bantam breeder to start a course of inbreeding (see Chapter 8).

When, after his first breeding season, he finds that all his stock is closely related because he now owns parents, and their offspring which are brothers and sisters, it becomes necessary to buy in a breeding male to head the pen in the following year.

It is at this point that the male is likely to prove more expensive than the original one; especially if the new bantam breeder has been highly successful at shows with young stock bred from the first pen.

It must not be overlooked that the best of the points of this stud have already been placed at the disposal of the beginner in the first

A good start can be made with a breeding trio of bantams, like these White Wyandottes

breeding trio. He will have to be prepared for a male of still higher quality to cost even more.

On the other hand, the beginner has the established breeder's brains available to him and many instances can be quoted where one successful exhibitor invariably obtains his new stock from the same original source.

If the new breeder has not enough advice or judgment to enable him to adopt Method 1 then Method 2 will serve him well.

It has often been said that those just starting with bantams should get a sitting of good hatching eggs from an established breeder and put them under a broody hen. They should then tend the hen, raise the chicks, see to the growing stock and show the best of them. Learning as they go through every process.

This is the gist of much that has been written in support of *Method 3*. There are difficulties in the way of this sort of start which did not always previously obtain. One is poor transport facilities for anything as fragile as hatching eggs. Second is the indifferent fertility of some breeds at some periods of the breeding season—probably just when eggs are most in demand. Third the fear that all the eggs will be from the same pen and that all chicks raised will be full brothers and sisters, thus making them unsuited for the following year's home breeding pen.

If good eggs can be got locally and taken by hand over a short distance, then a sitting might still make a suitable start always provided that it is understood that a new stock cockerel from the same source must be obtained to breed with any pullets reared from the eggs. The alternative is, if a first class cockerel is reared, to buy a couple of proven breeding hens to go with him. Either way, there will be heavier expenditure in the second season than there was for the hatching eggs.

Method 4, is to buy growing stock and complete their rearing in the new houses and runs which have been built (see Chapters 4 and 5). This is unsatisfactory both to buyer and seller. To the buyer because he may mar what the experienced breeder has already started, and then blame the breeder for it. Also because the breeder would not part with stock which had not yet developed final feathers, unless they were so poorly bred that he had not much use for them himself.

Unsatisfactory to the seller because, if he had a stud of highest repute, he could not determine which birds would make his best winners and would have to charge highly for all of them, to be on the safe side. He then might find that he had sent out stuff which turned a prospective customer into a dissatisfied grumbler, with neither party really to blame.

On the whole, this way cannot be recommended. If lack of experience or rearing facilities in the initial season compel the adoption of this method, the first purchase should be restricted to half a dozen growing pullets. From them the best two should be chosen and a cockerel bought from the same breeder to mate with them at a later date. In this way a fair breeding pen might be made up. But the really good stock can best be got together by adopting the first two methods described in these notes.

Chapter Four

METHODS OF HOUSING BANTAMS

There are as many ways of housing bantams as there are people keeping them—and most of them are correct.

Not many bantam breeders are content with ready-made houses. Nearly all of them become 'handy men' and make their own equipment to suit the needs of their particular breed or of the site available for bantam breeding. Some of these outfits are much better than others and most do their job quite well.

The essentials which have to be incorporated into design, no matter what size of house is needed, are a watertight roof, weatherproof sides, ratproof floor which is dry at all times and a structure which is free from draughts.

There is no need for bantam houses to be ugly. They need not be banished to the extreme end of the garden and have a screen erected to keep them out of sight. The outfit can be a focal point of interest.

Before passing to the breeding stud, it would be as well to look at what is wanted for those three or four bantams which are to be kept for ornamental purposes on the lawn. Their house need not be larger than 4 ft by 3 ft in area with a maximum height of 3½ ft. It should have some light by way of windows for those inclement days when the birds would be better indoors.

Fittings consist of a perch and droppings board, a couple of nestboxes, and drinker which cannot be spilled to make wetness on the floor, a feeding trough and grit box.

For mild and sheltered conditions a house with a 'Dixon' front would be suitable. Bantams would be healthy and fit in such a structure. Or a small house with a span roof, after the style of a doll's house in design, could have a mock thatched roof. That is, the roof would be covered with felt underneath to make it weatherproof but straw could be fixed to simulate thatch. This would be eminently suitable for small, brightly coloured bantams which would adorn the lawn.

The point of the 'Dixon'-type house is that it has a three-quarter span roof from the front lower edge of which small mesh netting is

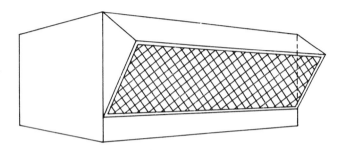

A house with a 'Dixon' front can easily be contrived by a handyman. Weather will not penetrate when wire netting is set as shown

stretched so that it slopes inwards to a retaining board at the bottom of the front of the house at an angle of 30° from the vertical.

In this connection it might be as well to consider the use of some of the new plastic mesh which is colourful and clean-looking.

Bantams in such a house will receive a maximum amount of fresh air but their floor and roosting quarters will be dry. Rain will not drive through the netting because, having hit the mesh front, it falls vertically to the ground and does not run down to the floor.

During the worst days of winter it would be an advantage if such a house could be set with its back to the prevailing storm. Alternatively, a light screen of plastic sheeting might be contrived with the object of shielding the bantams from the worst of the wind. But rain, sleet and snow would not matter.

Having suggested a 'doll's house' design as suitable for those bantams which are to form part of the garden scene it will be appreciated that this is not commercially available and must be made at home.

The floor should be slightly raised from the ground to maintain a dry state and the house should be movable, not being left on one site all the time.

For the more serious bantam breeder, who wishes to produce his own chicks and compete at the shows, the average back-garden outfit will consist of one unit for adult stock and another for rearing youngsters.

Both can be identical in size and pattern. An advantage would be that two houses could stand side by side and the access path could serve both. It would be a waste of room and effort to have the runs together and the houses at each extreme end of the outfit.

Nothing has yet been designed to beat the roosting shed with covered scratching shed attached. This sort of accommodation is suitable for layers, breeders, chicks and growing stock.

The bantams have shelter when they need it and reasonable exercising space. They can have a run in the kitchen garden as occasion permits and chicks can spend a little time on the garden or lawn, when their owner is present.

A very good pattern of house suitable for bantams under any conditions

The basis of room needed for each bantam, under these conditions, is 3 sq ft per bird. With this measure in mind, the unit can be designed to accommodate whatever is the 'norm.' desired. A 4 ft by 3 ft roosting house with scratching shed of the same size will hold eight bantams because they will not all be using the same part of the accommodation at the same time except when at roost. Thus the whole of the floor-space is available to every bantam during hours of daylight.

Having decided on the total number of adult bantams which will normally be kept, the owner can plan the size of his main unit accordingly.

It is best made under one roof. There are then no joints between house and scratching shed through which rain can drive.

The roosting portion should have the essentials of droppings board etc. already noted but the scratching shed portion would have only a weatherboard about 15 in deep, projecting at an angle of 45°. This would prevent rain from soaking floor litter with which the shed is provided.

At the bottom of the front a 6 in board would prevent litter from being thrown by the bantams through the netting and would help to check undue floor draughts.

The remainder of the front is covered with small mesh netting. This should be of such a size that sparrows and other birds could not get through and spread diseases. ½ in mesh would be about right.

The second unit is of precisely similar size and design. During the breeding season it will hold the balance of the adult stock until sufficient eggs are proved fertile and enough chicks hatched.

All the adults, to the full number, are then put together in the first house and scratching shed. The second one is thoroughly cleaned out

Simple but extremely useful, especially for a pair or trio
of Ornamental bantams

A series of fold units, specially designed for bantams, in ideal surroundings

and supplied with new litter. Growing stock, which has been initially reared in some small lawn unit, can then be accommodated and will continue in the same house until fully adult.

Where there is a really large garden, small orchard or other piece of land available, bantam breeding on a larger scale can take place.

The owner is now faced with the choice of two methods. He can either construct a large shed, divide it into sections and provide each section with a small, roofed run or he can adopt single units which are readily movable and have a quantity of them to house his birds.

Both methods serve well but the circumstances under which they are to be used normally will dictate which is preferable.

If a piece of garden is big enough for one good-sized permanent house but not for a considerable number of ark-type units, then the permanent building should be erected. This method is popular on the Continent and houses some very fine bantams there. It is also used by those favouring more than one breed here.

During bad weather there is a lot to be said for having all the bantams under one roof. And for headspace to be regulated to the height of the bantam breeder, so that he does not suffer discomfort when attending his stock.

Plans should take into account the need to accommodate adult breeding stock, spare adults, chicks, growers, exhibition bantams, spares, surplus males.

Each compartment should be not less than 5 ft by 4 ft. A little larger in each direction will be better. A continuous passage down the front or back of the house should be about 2 ft 6 in wide.

*Where garden space permits, one large house can be divided to
accommodate a stud of one breed*

Large windows are a necessity with this type of house, because
bantams are to be more or less permanently housed in it. They should
be adjustable to admit maximum draught-free ventilation in summer.

Each division should be solid for the first 2 ft and then consist of
small mesh netting. Interior fitments will consist of those items
previously named.

Given a small outdoor run for each division, fertility should be
quite good for most bantam breeds. Those which would succeed best
are sedate movers, not easily frightened and capable of adjusting their
lives to fairly close confinement.

As with the house, the runs should be solid for the first 2 ft and
afterwards be made from netting.

A couple of 20 ft long houses, set back to back, would occupy a
fairish piece of garden when outdoor runs were also provided and
would enable most bantam breeders to keep all the birds they had
time to see to. But for the man with good grassland at his disposal and
the wish to maintain a rather large stud, there is the method which
envisages the use of arks.

Each breeding pen is housed in an ark which consists of a roosting
and laying house about 3 ft square together with a wired run of

approximately double this size. Overall the ark measures 9 ft by 3 ft. The roosting section has a solid floor and contains nest-boxes which are accessible to the attendant from the outside but the run consists only of framework covered with wire netting.

The end of the run portion is solid and a short roof, about 2 ft long, will enable the drinker, food container and grit box to be kept in the dry.

These arks are good for breeding stock and getting bantams to the peak of fitness. They are not ideal for egg production or those birds which have masses of profuse feather.

The total number being known, the land intended for them should be measured to ensure that each ark can be moved by its own width every day so that the bantams have a clean patch of land for each day's run. Rotation should be so that at least a fortnight elapses

Extensive outfit for breeding and rearing several breeds
in large numbers

before the first patch is again occupied. In the meantime the thick of the droppings should have been taken up from it and the area lightly powdered with hydrated lime.

Appliances of this type are also good for chicks growing into adults but are a little awkward for chick rearing in the early stages, unless this operation is by natural methods. Growers would, in fact, be better in larger groups and larger runs but could be successfully managed under this method.

The man who contemplates bantams on a really extensive scale will not have the time to move arks around and needs a permanent layout of a different nature to that suggested for the large back garden.

His main consideration is that appliances stand with their backs to prevailing winds of the district and that all houses are of one pattern so that interchanging spare parts etc. will not present a problem.

A traditional pattern, the 6 ft by 4 ft lean-to, serves best. Each house is 6 ft long, 4 ft wide and 4 ft high at front. There is an attendant's door at one side of the front together with a drop-down window over an aperture covered with wire netting and topped with a weatherboard. A pophole for the bantams is in the front and the house stands towards one end of a rather extensive grass run.

It is usual to site the houses so that they are easily accessible from one main walk through the whole of the field. Each one must have the usual fittings, droppings board, perch, nest-boxes, food trough, drinker and grit-box.

Some breeders believe in lifting their houses well off the ground and permitting the bantams the extra shelter afforded by the space underneath which also becomes the communal dust bath. Others have the houses set firmly on the ground and place wire netting from the base, into the ground, so that bantams and rats are both excluded.

This summary of principal patterns of housing, suitable for varying circumstances, is capable of endless variations. What will be suitable for one man would be disliked by another. But the basic requirements are there and can readily be adapted.

Whichever is chosen for whatever purpose it should be borne in mind that bantams can multiply pretty quickly and many owners cannot bring themselves to part with the good old ones in spite of having bred some good young ones, as well. When the outfit is first put together and initial stock installed, the plant should be only one quarter full. To start with well filled houses and be limited in room is the short cut to disaster from overcrowding.

Chapter Five

OTHER USEFUL EQUIPMENT

Although all the houses described in the previous chapter would also serve for bantams being immediately prepared for exhibition, it is better to have some units designed for that purpose. These are usually referred to as 'cockerel boxes' although they do, in fact, serve for both males and females on occasion.

Cockerels are usually housed individually, after reaching full maturity, but pullets are run in pairs. The cockerel box is a small, lean-to house about 3 ft square, with a covered run about 4 ft by 3 ft.

The house is well littered with dry sawdust and a perch is provided. A drinking vessel and feeding trough are fitted inside the house.

There may be a small window at one side of the attendant's door and ventilation must be adequate. A hinged shutter above the door is suitable.

The main use of the cockerel box is to keep bantams in good feather, free from weathering and staining. It must, therefore, be used with discretion or the purpose will be defeated. The birds should be confined to the house portion when sunlight is intense and only allowed to use the run during the evening or early morning of summer days.

Although many bantams will be conditioned in the large divisions of the penning room (see Chapter 10) there will be as many which will need to have a cockerel box provided for them during summer weather. A small row could be devised by building one structure and dividing it into sections, putting the attendant's doors in the back instead of the front.

From time to time a bantam will go down with some minor ailment.

It is as well to be prepared for these and to have a 'hospital' available. It does not matter whether it is on the lines of the penning room, but in smaller scale, or a range of pens put together under a sound roof, outdoors.

Either will serve as long as it is understood that only those birds with slight ailments should be treated and they should not be housed with others which are healthy, until thoroughly cured.

Serious illnesses can rarely be properly treated by home-doctoring methods. If the services of a veterinary surgeon are not available or the bantam is not very valuable, it should be painlessly destroyed and the carcase incinerated. A small range of four pens for hospital purposes would measure no more than 4 ft long by 4 ft high by 2 ft from back to front, each pen being 2 ft all ways.

Bantam show baskets will be required. These are made to traditional sizes and can be had to hold one, two, three or four bantams, in usual sizes. They are well made and suitable for the job of transporting birds to and from shows.

The baskets are lined with hessian and afford adequate ventilation in summer. During winter it may be advisable to underline the lids with stiff, brown paper and to place a thickness of sacking material right round the outside of the wickerwork.

If containers are made at home for this purpose, using plywood or similar materials, care will have to be taken that bases are firm and ventilation adequate. Should boxes become stuffy during summer,

Useful for cockerel boxes, these units can also accommodate chicks and growing stock

bantams will rapidly lose condition and go into a premature moult.

One advantage of making containers is that the size of each compartment can be regulated to the breed kept. Thus, a box for Modern Game could have smaller but taller sections than one for Pekins, in which the divisions would be further apart.

If manufactured food troughs, generally of galvanised metal, are used they should be bought as for growing stock (large breeds) and

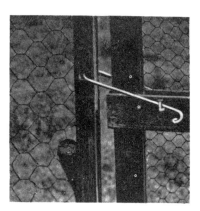

Handy and easily made gate fastener for use when the gate need not be locked

not for adults. These will suit most bantams better than the very large units usually offered.

Most people knock their own troughs together from two side pieces of wood nailed onto two end pieces. This results in a V-shaped trough with rectangular ends which allow it to stand firmly on the ground. When not in use, all such troughs should be turned upside down so that bantams do not perch on the edges and foul the insides.

Drinking vessels come in all shapes and sizes. As long as a constant supply of clean, cold water is available it does not really matter what shape the vessels are.

For preference, they should be adapted to the breeds kept. What would suit a Sussex might not be suitable for a Poland and this would be particularly so if the drinker had a small aperture through which the bantam had to push its head before it could drink.

A tip for crested and bearded bantams, if open drinkers are favoured, is to fix a grid of 1 in mesh wire over the top so that mufflings, beards and crests are mostly kept out of the water when bantams drink. It goes without saying that the level of water should be well maintained.

Grit boxes can be simply made so that a small hopper is full of grit which falls into a little trough as the bantams peck at the material. Again, because these are home-made they can be adjusted to the needs of a particular breed.

It is wasteful to offer grit from a large, open vessel. All the choicest pieces of right size are taken first and much of the remainder scattered as bantams throw it aside to get the portions they want.

Chapter Six

MANAGEMENT AND FEEDING OF ADULT BANTAMS

Stock management is largely based on common sense and some basic rules which apply to all bantams, whatever their breed and for whatever purpose they are kept.

What is learned when the first pen of birds is installed also applies, in greater degree, when numbers have been multiplied and the stud is established at maximum capacity.

Regular attention is a necessity. The keeping of small livestock cannot be left to chance. Attention must be regular and mealtimes met without fail. Bantams depend on their owner for all their wants. They cannot be turned out into a field to graze and left for a few days—even supposing a field is available.

Those who set out to keep bantams should realise that they owe a duty to the birds to keep them clean and healthy and to provide them with the necessities of life regularly. If they are not prepared to do this; if absences from home cannot be covered by some well disposed neighbour, then such people had better not embark on bantam keeping as a hobby.

MANAGEMENT

Each day the droppings board in the roosting house should be scraped down and the manure removed to the compost heap, away from the house where the bantams are kept.

The good stockman can tell much about his birds by glancing at the state of the droppings board each morning. If there are soft-shelled eggs which have been dropped during the night, traces of blood or worms in the droppings or those which are yellow and frothy instead of being firm and slightly capped with white, he recognises the symptoms and can take appropriate measures.

Instead of the scraping of the droppings board being considered a somewhat repulsive chore, it should be thought of as a ready indication of the state of health of the bantams in that house.

Having been scraped, the droppings board should then be lightly strewn with sand or sawdust. Fine peat moss could also be used. Any of these substances will blend suitably in the compost heap and, eventually, be suitable for the garden.

The use of lime is not recommended. It will free ammonia from fresh droppings when they fall during the night and the air will become fouled, doing the bantams no good at all.

Having dealt with this matter, the drinking vessels should be filled with clean cold water. The only exception would be in the depth of winter when water would have the chill taken from it. This has nothing to do with preventing it from freezing but simply makes the water more palatable to the birds so that they take in a quantity when it is first served and so keep better condition.

A quick glance at the grit box, which should contain both hard grit, for digestive purposes, and limestone or shell grit to assist in the formation of soundly shelled eggs, and morning day-to-day management is completed. The grit box should always be kept replenished and small particles and dust cleared from it. Bantams will not use this material even if no other is given.

In the long term there are other points of management which ought to be learned and carried out. A dust bath is necessary for the good health of those bantams which are not taken up and washed or otherwise cleaned for show. This enables the birds to wallow and throw the dust through their feathers. Then, by shaking themselves vigorously, their plumage is rid of many pests and attains good order.

The dust bath need only be a wooden box about 1 ft 6 in square and 6 in deep. It should be filled with dry, finely sifted earth to which a dash of disinfectant powder has been added. Bantams will not need to be taught how to use it. If the box is placed under cover outside or under the droppings board in the house it will soon be in constant use. The material in it should be cleaned and replenished as required.

As a matter of routine the bantam keeper should go into the poultry shed at night, when the bantams are at roost. He should take each bird in hand and examine it for signs of scaly leg, lice or mite. If any are found, treatment should be carried out.

At the same time it will be possible to check up on bodily condition. If birds are light in weight, the remedy is either more or better quality food. If too heavy, it is not difficult to adjust the amount until birds resume normal condition.

Ventilation is important and it is a point of management that the atmosphere within each house is sampled as soon as the door is open. If stuffy, more air is needed. If there is a buoyant draught, the intake of fresh air should be reduced. Bantams will show whether they are in a good atmosphere which suits them by the manner in which they are at rest on their perches.

Happy, comfortable birds will have sleek plumage and many will be asleep with heads tucked under wings. If they are sat with ruffled feathers, especially in winter, then conditions are usually too bleak.

Routine inspections of the kind suggested, undertaken at monthly intervals, will tell the bantam owner all that he wants to know about the condition of his stock and he will learn something new from each visit.

Litter for each house floor is of some importance. It can be of any substance which will enable the birds to scratch amongst it without hurting their legs and feet and which does not become dusty to cause nasal irritation.

It is usual to find straw, chaff, autumn leaves from oak and beech trees, chopped bracken which has been cut and stacked, peat moss litter, white wood shavings or heavy sawdust on the floors of bantam houses.

When it has become very soiled or contains a lot of feathers, the whole of the litter should be removed and a new lot put in. Or, in the case of peat moss and sawdust, it can be riddled, the droppings etc. removed and a new lot added to the best of the old.

In any case, there should be an annual cleanout when all movable fittings are also removed, the whole spring cleaned on a good, drying day and everything made 'as new'. At this time the opportunity will be taken to whitewash, creosote or paint the inside of each house to restore it to good condition.

FEEDING

Usual question is how much each bird should have to eat at each meal. This is one which cannot be answered firmly. Many points arise. Which breed? For what purpose is it kept? How is it housed? All these things have a bearing but a general guide can be given and this

Troughs should always be used for feeding bantams, even when on extensive range as this mixed flock is

must be adapted according to the size and nature of the breed and whether or not it lays many eggs.

For convenience, because so many bantam keepers are in a hurry to go to work each morning, it is suggested that this is the appropriate time to give a feed of corn to the birds.

For the larger breeds, miniatures of large fowl, two closed handfuls of grain will serve every three bantams. The grain should be scattered in the litter on the floor of the house so that the birds have to scratch to find it. This is a quick, convenient method which promotes exercise among the bantams and ensures that they do not immediately stand about in idleness while their owner is absent at work. For smaller breeds, such as the old-established ornamental sorts, the amount could be one closed handful for every two bantams. If grain is fed at night there is some risk of some of it being left in the litter after dusk and attracting mice and rats—arch enemies of the wellbeing of bantams.

As a staple diet the best grain is sound wheat. This is usually foreign grain and rather harder than English grown wheat. Clipped oats come a good second and may be given once or twice weekly, as an alternative, to keep appetites sharp. If the bantams have no white plumage some finely kibbled maize can be given especially to hard feathered breeds, during winter months. This should be carefully regulated in quantity, otherwise the birds will become internally fat. Barley is not usually fed as a staple grain and is rather coarse for most bantams.

Although mixed corn is somewhat cheaper than buying each kind separately it is not recommended because the bantams tend to pick out what they like best and leave the rest in the litter. A supply of greenfood should be arranged. This should be given about midday. If young, tender stuff such as lettuce is available it can be given whole and the birds left to peck it as they want it. The greenstuff should be hung from a hook at about a foot from the ground. If thrown down it becomes soiled and may start crop troubles.

Older greenstuff, such as leaves from cabbage and cauliflower, which has become tough should be shredded and fed from a trough. This ensures a greater intake and helps good health. An alternative for use during winter is half a swede turnip or red beetroot impaled on a blunt spike. The bantams will peck the succulent flesh from the middle and leave the rind on the spike, to be removed to the compost heap each night.

The main feed of the day, which will do most to determine the health of the flock, will be given in the early evening. During the long hours of spring and summertime there is no problem in keeping an eye on the bantams and checking on their appetites. During winter, when darkness falls early, this feed will usually have to be given by artificial light. The problem is then a little more difficult as some bantams turn lazy and go back to their perches as soon as their first requirements are met.

Many bantam breeders still use wet mash for the evening feed. This is one of three choices to ensure a balanced diet for the birds. The others are simpler but, in the eyes of many, not as capable of close control.

Good wet mash should be crumbly (friable) in texture and easily taken up from a trough by the bantams. To gauge the amount needed for a given number of birds, sufficient should be mixed to fill a trough and this should be left before the bantams for 15-20 min. If, at the end of that time, they still look eagerly for more food and are obviously not satisfied with full crops, the amount should be increased. If there is mash left, this should be taken away and the amount adjusted for following evenings.

To make a good wet mash a base is needed and this should be dried off by adding meal and stirring well. The base can consist of biscuit meal which has been soaked in water for an hour before use. To achieve a degree of economy stale bread can be made into rusk in the oven, broken into small pieces and soaked in cold water, then drained and used as a base. Secondary economy can be gained by using household scraps of cooked meat, minced fairly finely, and left-over vegetables. This material should also be dried off with meal, until it becomes crumbly.

Meals which are used for drying off should be made for a purpose by competent millers. Proprietary brands are best because their manufacture is supervised by nutritional experts who see that the right amounts of trace elements and vitamins are incorporated.

Layers' mash and Breeders' mash can be used as the drying-off meal, according to season and the purpose for which bantams are being kept. It may reasonably be argued that some of the 'balance' of the complete meal is impaired when used with a base or house scraps. This is true, but most bantams are kept for exhibition and it is not vital to the success of the stud that the maximum number of eggs be laid within a minimum space of time.

An alternative, which will ensure that the bantams get a balanced diet only but which precludes economies suggested, is to use a good brand of either Layers' or Breeders' pellets. These can either be given from a trough at feeding time, as with wet mash; left in an open hopper available to the bantams all day, or scattered in the litter as a second scratch feed. Some breeders economise a little by mixing some wheat with the pellets and scattering the mixture in the litter.

Pellets are manufactured by the same people that make the meals and have similar formulas for different purposes.

The last method, now much out of favour but still persisted in by a few, is to offer dry meal from an open hopper throughout the day. If the bantams take in sufficient food they are well served but if some of those breeds which have facial adornments get rather tired of constant uncomfortable pecking at the meal they tend to undereat and so lose condition.

Having regard to the small quantities required by bantam keepers it is inadvisable to buy in bulk quantities or to try to mix meals at home. The millers do the job so much better that the little extra expense is well worth while.

Chapter Seven

SELECTING AND MATING UP
BREEDING STOCK

The same basic principles apply to all breeds of bantams when selection of breeding stock and their matching are under review.

It is assumed that all the birds are purebred and conform, within reason, to the requirements laid down in the appropriate Breed Standard. Points for consideration are:

1. Health
2. Conformation, including bone structure
3. Breed character
4. Colour
5. Headpoints.

Bantams which have suffered from any disease which has necessitated severe treatment should not be used for breeding. It may well be that their offspring will not get the same trouble but it is indicative of weakness that the birds have been seriously ill at all.

Those which have mild, seasonal disorders such as slight running colds will not be affected for breeding purposes.

Good health can be seen as well as felt, when bantams are being selected. Their feathers will be sleek, well made and form a protective covering likely to serve them well during heavy storms. Birds will have a healthy glow about the head. There will be no discolouration or weakness apparent. In most varieties combs, faces, wattles and lobes will be bright red. Exceptions are in those breeds where some other colour of face is demanded by the Standard e.g. gipsy faces in Brown-red Modern Game.

Quartette of Minorcas headed by a very virile looking sire

The prospective sire should be taken in hand and a check made that he has bright headpoints. There should be no discolouration or darkening of the comb as he is handled. This might indicate liver or heart trouble. Or it might only indicate over-fatness which can be checked by assessing the amount of flesh along the breastbone and its hardness. There should be no wheezing, when the bird is held in the hand. Respiratory or heart trouble indicated if this occurs.

The face should be open with a pleasant expression. Eyes should be bright and stand out well from the head. The sire should have plumage which is normal for the breed. For preference, each feather should be wide, well made, whole and resilient. Tail furnishings should be plentiful, according to Standard.

Odd exceptions as in Modern Game, should be known.

Continue to examine the sire as to legs and feet. Bone should be sound, neat and refined. No breed should have coarse shanks and thick scales. Texture will also be shown in tight, well fitting scales which continue down the toes. Nails should be reasonably short and firm. Birds with long, thin toe nails are often bad doers.

Any deformity, bent toes, duck feet (in which the back toe does not stand out in line but tends towards the front of the foot) or toes which are too short to support the bird when standing normally should spell rejection.

Holding the bantam in both hands and balancing him evenly his tail should be checked for wryness. If it is carried to one side consistently, rounded formation of the back should be suspected and checked. This fault 'roach back' and wry tail are hereditary and would be transmitted to offspring. Either should result in a bird being rejected from the breeding flock.

Look at the nostrils to see that they are open and clean. Many troubles can arise from an accumulation of thick mucus at this point. Examine the vent and surrounding area to ensure there is no discharge or scabbing, both of which could be transmitted to hens during the breeding season.

A check should be made for mites or lice, the nits of which form a greyish mass at the feather roots, especially round the vent. If found, good treatment is by way of nicotine sulphate perch paint sold as a ready-made product to be used according to makers' instructions. Afterwards each bantam should be checked and any masses removed from their fluff before being put in the breeding pens.

Finally, watch the prospective sire on the run. He should move well, being on balance all the time. When his feet are firmly on the ground he should stand 'four square', defying the world and the weather.

Females should be handled and checked for the same points. Additionally their pelvic bones should be tested to ensure that they are fine and pliable. If covered with hard gristle or fat birds should be

Breeding pens should consist of bantams of level quality as demonstrated by this pen of Buff Pekins

kept from the breeding pen until they have been slimmed. But no amount of slimming will make a coarse bantam into a refined one and thickness should not be mistaken for fatness.

All the bantams having passed the handling test for health and conformation—one operation as described above—they should be scrutinised for breed character. Every breed has a Standard to which it must conform and every prospective breeding bantam must carry good points to accord with its breed name. It may be that some bantams, especially older hens and adult cocks, are rather large. But they are full of character and good breeding.

This extra size is no bar to using them in the breeding pen. Their offspring will be of normal size, especially if hatched rather late in the season.

Oversized cockerels and pullets should not be used freely. They will be even larger after an adult moult. Being vigorous they are likely to breed lusty chicks which will grow into even bigger bantams. If a biggish cockerel has to be chosen because of his general character he should be mated with adult hens of the right size.

A head study showing all the quality points needed for breeding

Colour must be of the sort described in Breed Standards. To attempt to grade up to Standard colour by using bantams which are somewhat deficient and improving by selection is to undertake work which has already been done by other breeders.

Most bantams used in the breeding pen should be as well coloured as their brothers and sisters which are exhibited. Indeed, the head of a breeding pen should be as good as a showbird in all but size or, better still, he should be an actual winner which is still fit and vigorous.

When bantams of the right shade cannot be mated together it might be possible to 'get away with it' in one season by mating light to dark shades. But this should be considered as a temporary expedient only and not as standard practice.

It is necessary to look over headpoints carefully because few standards exist which do not give a fair share of points to formation of comb, lobes and wattles. The male must be good in head. His comb must accord with the Standard and be free from imperfections. If it is not, the weaknesses which he shows will be transmitted to many of his progeny.

In the case of breeds with small, single combs defects in females will not readily show up. But they will be latent and will recur in cockerels of the following generation, often intensified to a great degree.

Texture of comb and face as well as wattles is important. Best appearance is that described as 'hard roe'. Thin, glossy skin in not wanted and in those breeds which have white lobes will soon yield to white in face—a serious defect in showing and breeding.

After all the bantams have passed tests and are considered up to standard and fit for breeding the question arises of how many females should run with a male. In the small, ornamental breeds which give most fertile eggs after the sun has gained some power in spring, one mate will be suitable for most males, especially if they have been shown much. A fairly safe rule is to mate an adult cock with a good pullet or a strong, matured cockerel to a couple of adult hens.

It is often said that the good points of one sex should be offset by the weaknesses of the other. In practice, in small inbred studs, the same points are obvious on both sides of the pen. Surest way to progress is by using birds which are similar in quality and possessing no bad faults.

Established miniatures, rather more vigorous and capable of producing fertile eggs earlier in the season can be mated in pens of four. With a sound male and three healthy females there will be more various near-relatives in future breeding seasons.

If it is thought that any male is more vigorous than his mates would like and he is harrying them too much (a cause of infertility which is sometimes not recognised) a hen of another sort, laying a distinctive egg, can be added to the pen. Her eggs are not hatched, of course, although they will be fertile.

Only the newer, larger breeds which are mostly noted for their laying powers will be mated in pens of 6 or 7 birds. The object here is to get as many chicks as possible from which to select those of high quality. When they fine down and are less robust, the number of females which will run with one male is reduced.

When heavy breed miniatures are kept there will be some broodiness during late spring and early summer. It is usual to add an extra hen in such pens so that there will still be a reasonable supply of hatching eggs when needed, even after a couple of hens have become broody and gone out of lay.

Having put the stock bantams together, eggs should be checked for shape, size and shell texture. The better the egg the more chance it has of producing a robust chick, if fertile. Hens habitually laying eggs which are very porous or have ridges and bumps around them should be penned alone and kept on short rations until losing some of their internal fat which is, almost certainly, causing the bother. If hens do not improve it may be concluded that they suffer from some derangement of the oviduct and must be excluded from breeding operations.

If egg shape and texture are neglected the strain will gradually deteriorate until there are more weak and infertile eggs than there are good ones.

Upon laying commencing, fertile eggs may be expected within ten to fourteen days. If the male is already running with pullets it is possible that their eggs will be fertile from first laying. It is not necessary for the male to copulate with each female daily. He can fertilise several eggs at one time if there is free access for the sperm to travel to the ovary.

It is not possible to determine from the actions of the bantams how many eggs will be fertile but, if stock is selected on the lines indicated and allowed to settle down in the breeding pens the percentage of fertile eggs should be quite high.

Chapter Eight

INBREEDING—OUTCROSSING—
STRAIN-MAKING

Much mysticism has been wrapped round the subject of inbreeding by past writers. Older authors wrote at length about the virtues of 'blood'. The newer school tends to describe homozygotes and base their operations on the Theory of Mendelism.

Somewhere between the two is a relatively simple, straightforward definition which can be understood by all concerned with the breeding of bantams. There is also a formula which can be applied, when strain-making is discussed.

Inbreeding means the mating together of bantams which are related. Generally, there is some sort of system which a breeder favours and some outstanding bantam to which all the birds go back. But, if the birds mated together in a breeding pen are related at all, there is some measure of inbreeding. The bantams are homozygous.

Outcrossing is employed when birds which appear to be unrelated are mated together. Their offspring are heterozygous. It is as well to mention, at this point, that few bantams will be utterly unrelated because the basic first stock is almost always the pool from which all studs have drawn their foundation stock. For all practical purposes, bantams are regarded as unrelated when they are known to have originated in two different establishments in different parts of the country. The success of some of these 'outcrosses' is due, not to the bantams being unrelated but to them having common ancestry in the past. Having been reared in different places and by different methods they come together with renewed vigour and so are successful in producing winning stock.

Strain-making takes place when a breeder seeks to establish a line of his own from which results can reasonably be forecast. There must be a definite programme for this undertaking.

When a breeder deliberately starts to inbreed to one outstanding bird he must make sure that the virtues of all the bantams employed are of the best quality. Inbreeding has limitations in that it can only 'lock in' those qualities that exist. It cannot produce anything new. At times, there will be what appear to be definite advances and those bantams which show them should be used for breeding. These steps forward occur when all the good points of both parents combine and their weaknesses are held in the background.

Under a system of inbreeding there will, from time to time, be 'throw backs' which will horrify their breeder. These occur when the weaknesses which were 'locked in' with the original parents combine to push the virtues into the background. Needless to say, such bantams should not be used for breeding.

Inbreeding will preserve all the good points which were evident in the original pen. It is up to the breeder to produce sufficient chicks each year to enable him to make a selection, some of which will again carry those good points.

Line-breeding is rather better, when external show points are the main criterion of quality. A superb bantam is used as the cornerstone of this method. A champion cock is mated to two or three selected hens. If a small ornamental breed, he may be mated to them at different times throughout the breeding season. A larger breed can run with all the hens at once, provided their eggs can be identified and chicks marked.

Immediately after the first breeding season there must be a number of individual pairs of bantams mated, all of them related. In the second season pairs might consist of the original cock to three pullets, one from each hen in, say, three successive months. The original hens to separate cockerels. A cockerel from one hen to a pullet from another and so on.

The permutation of matings, related to each other, is quite large. Unless pullets are mated back to the outstanding male in the first possible breeding season, his influence will rapidly wane. In the first year he is 50% of all his offspring. In each succeeding year this will be diluted by one-half unless careful matings are made and records kept.

Line-breeding demands this sort of care and accurate records if it is to succeed.

Closed family breeding is a form of inbreeding not likely to be greatly used by bantam men. Briefly, it means that males are used only if the females which are their sisters give a good family performance. In the case of show bantams which are bred to win, three or four sisters would all have to win prizes before the male was placed at the head of a breeding pen.

This method is of great value to those concerned with egg production where the laying records of the pullets dictate the breeding value of the cockerels.

In the course of time, with inbreeding generally but more especially with line-breeding, there will be a noticeable 'family likeness' running

Family likeness by inbreeding is readily seen in a pen
of White Pekins

through the bantams in one yard. This will be especially so when culling has been accurate and selection made carefully.

At this time the breeder can congratulate himself that he has got to the point where 'like breeds like', always making allowances for those 'throw backs' in which all the bad points of the stud combine, and are seen.

Selection should now be based on five important considerations:

1. Standard requirements
2. Family likeness
3. Performance
4. Conformation
5. Health.

The *Standard requirements* for the breed being known, it is pointless to include any bantam in the breeding pen which does not conform

*Light Sussex pullets are 'birds of a feather' from
the same parents*

and which cannot possibly win prizes or come very near to that goal.

Family likeness means that the general appearance of all members of
the stud shall be similar, making careful note of the fact that while
the birds have the same points of beauty they also have the same
defects.

Performance is decided by the winning of prizes, laying ability of the
females, fertility of the males, hatchability, rearability, rate of maturity
and ease of feathering. Not a target likely to be easily achieved and all
points of importance which make the difference between success and
failure. In the long term, bantams must be virile if they are to stay the
course and help give the variety a reputation for reliability.

Conformation and *health* were dealt with in Chapter 7 and are more
necessary in inbred stock than any other form of bantams.

The born stockman knows, as soon as he handles a bantam, that it
accords with his mental ideals. He notes how a bird rides in the hand,
how it feels to the touch, how it walks on the run. Others, without
this flair, can acquire skill by persistent handling of their birds and
noting every detail and reaction, both in times of high condition and,
perhaps, poor health.

One or two points on inbreeding which ought to be carried out by
those embarking on this system. All young stock should be permanently marked. The Poultry Club closed rings are ideal for this

purpose. There should be a book record of the season's operations. The temptation to oversell bantams of high merit should be resisted. 'Cornerstone' stock, with the virtues of the original foundation male, should always be kept for breeding.

Outcrossing, while not always literally true because of distant relationship of many bantams, is often used by the one pen man who only has room for a couple of broods of chicks each year. He wishes to maintain virility in his stock and buys in a new stock male every second year or so.

If he gets them from all parts and different breeders he cannot possibly foretell what quality offspring will be. He could be lucky enough to get a really good winner. He may go for several seasons with nothing but second-raters.

His best plan is to make an arrangement with a large breeder to supply a stock male as required and always go back to the same source. In this way, although the small man regards it as outcrossing, he is, in fact, using an uncontrolled method of inbreeding. All the males which he gets will have some degree of relationship and, in time, his own birds will be related to them.

Strength will be improved by bringing in a well-reared, vigorous stock cockerel. Quality will improve by the use of something produced by a top breeder who is, undoubtedly, basing his breeding operations on inbreeding.

To the careful bantam breeder, nothing can equal the interest to be got by strain-making. The basis of this method is to obtain stock of the highest quality from each of two sources which have been identified as having bantams which will be complementary to each other.

The strengths of one stud should be offset against the weaknesses of the other, as far as this is possible. Both original breeding pens should be of the best because both can be used equally in all future breeding operations.

If circumstances or finances demand that one pen shall be of much better quality than the other, then strain-making must be modified so that the best quality bantams are used to greatest advantage.

It needs care to see that this is done. It needs pre-planning and careful recording. But, in the end, the results will be such that the new strain is in a relatively unassailable position and can immediately take its place at the shows alongside the two leading studs which provided the foundation stock. Care should be taken to ensure that the original parent stock is healthy as close mating is necessary in the earliest stages. At the same time, it might reasonably be expected that the crossing of two strains will bring additional vigour.

This can result in offspring of the first generation being more robust than refined and there may be minor disappointment. Matters will tend to right themselves in the following breeding season.

In buying two breeding pairs from different sources bantams which are much dissimilar should be avoided. Pairs of reasonable excellence in all points should be sought.

To illustrate the method a simple pedigree is set out. This extends over three generations, obtained from two pairs of birds.

These two strains of foundation stock are crossed and, for the purpose of illustrating the exercise, it is assumed that male A is the top quality cock and the cornerstone of the stud.

One pair is male A and female B and the other, from another source, male Y and female Z.

By blending the strains in the first year there will be cockerel and pullet progeny which will each bear AZ and YB blood in equal proportions. Two breeding pens in the second year will cause the A line to be diluted to one-quarter. That is, AZ mated to YB would give AZYB in equal parts while a cockerel YB to pullets AZ would give progeny with identical value in pedigree (see Top Fig., p. 45).

The following year, mating AZYB male to YBAZ females (or vice versa) would result in all four original parents being equally represented. Such matings could continue for many generations but at no time would the excellent original male A have more influence than one-quarter.

This gives inbreeding by the shortest method but lacks the flexibility of the second scheme and prevents a dominant bantam being used to greatest advantage.

The original idea was to make the very best use of male A and stamp his quality on most youngsters. Method shown by Lower Fig., p. 45, ensures that a new strain is formed within four years and the bantams in it carry the blood of male A to the proportion of 7/16ths.

This is achieved by line-breeding in one pen and the complete blending, outlined in Fig. 1 pedigree, in the other.

Progeny from the first mating is, again, AZ. The best of these females are handled for breed points, conformation, health etc. as already described in this book and mated back to their sire. He is described as AA or A(2) because he contributes two quarters.

The resultant progeny is AAAZ or A(3)Z(1). The figures in brackets show the proportion of each parent's 'blood', as the phrase runs amongst practical bantam breeders. A male of this breeding is then mated back to his dam and her sisters. As they now contribute four-eighths she is labelled A(2)Z(2) or, out in full, AAZZ.

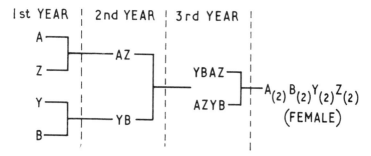

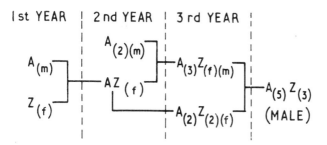

It must be appreciated that in the first generation each parent contributes one-half and this is again halved in each succeeding generation unless one of these birds is bred back.

An original 'pure strain' bought for the foundation pens is best expressed as equivalent to two quarters, four eighths or eight sixteenths, as the case may be.

If the final products from the two pens described by pedigrees illustrated above (first three years) are blended together, the resulting stock will contain the following proportions of blood in their veins— $A(7)Z(5)Y(2)B(2)$. This results in the excellent male A being dominant to the extent of 7/16ths or nearly half. In this way the fourth generation offspring should most closely resemble the excellence of the best of the original foundation stock but still have points from the second source which were thought desirable.

By pre-planning and working out pedigrees on paper before ever the first initial pen is mated any variation to any particular strength in parent stock can be made.

After the final-blend has been made it may reasonably be assumed that any bantam within the stud will mate well with any other and that 'like will produce like' to a marked degree.

It will be appreciated that the two strains which were first bought were crossed at once and those which were not of the highest quality were not subsequently re-introduced, although the excellent male A was. One word of warning here—it is highly probable that winners equal to the original stock were not produced in the first two generations. But even better birds could be expected if the method were strictly applied and the breeder did not panic. His fourth generation bantams should be a joy to look at and a credit to his skill.

Chapter Nine

FROM THE EGG TO POINT OF MATURITY

Separate appliances are needed for use during the breeding season in order to hatch chicks and rear them. The one thing that all these gadgets have in common is that they must be scrupulously clean before use and restored to that condition as soon as possible afterwards, being stored away when not in use.

If left about they will deteriorate rapidly and will give chicks a poor start in life by harbouring germs.

If the natural method of hatching and rearing is favoured and suitable broody hens are to be had in season, the only appliances needed will be sitting boxes and rearing coops.

The former will be of a size to suit the sort of hens used. They will, obviously, need to be of largest size for hens of large breeds such as Sussex and Wyandottes. Smallest sitting boxes will be those intended for bantams, intermediate size being suitable for Silkie-crossbreds.

The largest box will be about 16 in wide by 18 in deep and have a height of 18 in. There will be a retaining board at the bottom of the front to which is hinged a lid which will be secured to the top of the box. Ventilation holes will be suitably arranged and the lid will let down to form a walking-on board so that the broody hen can gently return to her eggs after feeding.

Rearing coops can either be of the traditional slatted fronted sort—as used for pheasant rearing—or can be specially contrived to suit the site on which chicks will be reared. The slatted front coop is quite suitable where chicks can run out on grass but not as good for confined conditions.

In back-garden bantam plants the owner usually has his own ideas

47

of the sort of appliance wanted and makes something with a small, wire covered run attached. The run portion may even have a solid roof so that the appliance may also serve for growing stock or conditioning a show bantam.

Management for natural hatching and rearing is, first to ensure that the hen is properly broody and likely to sit out the required period of three weeks, afterwards rearing her chicks. When becoming broody she will remain on the nest for a long time after laying an egg. Eventually, she will choose to remain on the nest altogether. When approached she will ruffle her plumage and give the typical clucking noise or 'croon' repeatedly.

When it is realised that a broody hen is available the nest-box should be prepared and a nest made within it. Take some moist earth (free from worms and pests) and bank up the four corners of the nest-box, making a saucer shaped base. A good handful of long straw should be twisted to form a 'rope' and this should be arranged in an oval. Soft meadow hay should then be used to top off the nest and a couple of dummy eggs placed in it.

When the hen is fully broody she should be dusted with insect powder and removed to the prepared nest at nightfall. She should be left until the following evening when it will be necessary to remove her for food and water, and to relieve herself.

In the meantime hatching eggs should be placed in the nest, an odd number being preferred. The hen should be allowed to walk on to them, when she will sit gently and 'shuffle' the eggs about until they are all tucked underneath her body.

If it is apparent that she could safely cover more eggs than have been given another one or two may be added, as long as they are tucked away like the others. If all the eggs are not satisfactorily covered, one or two should be taken away at once.

It is not possible to lay down any hard and fast rule as to the number of eggs a broody will cover. A small bantam may take as few as half a dozen while a large, comfortable, matronly hen of proven ability will cover eighteen.

If fresh at the time of sitting, bantam eggs will hatch about the 19th day, the hatch being finished by the 20th. For large bantams of more recent extraction with a lot of large-breed blood in them, eggs will take a day longer to hatch. It is rare that they go the full 21 days, as in the case of large fowl.

Eggs should be tested by holding them in front of a light, shielded from other light by the cupped hands or by using a piece of stout cardboard with a hole cut in it, at the end of the 7th day of sitting.

Those which are fertile will be quite opaque while the infertiles will show as 'clears'—that is they will still look as though newly laid. Clears and doubtfuls which are not fully fertile should be removed. A further test at the end of the 12th day should establish which are fertile beyond all reasonable doubt. Others which will prove to be addled—the germ has ceased to develop—should also be removed.

Unless the sitting box has been placed in a very dry place with draughts or free ventilation, hatching arrangements can safely be left to Nature. If it is thought that the nest is too dry, it will be sufficient slightly to damp the underparts of the hen with water applied by hand on the evening of the 15th and 17th days. This should be done just before the hen returns to the nest.

After the eggs have started to chip, which is when the chicks are making their first move towards emerging from their shells, the

Newly hatched chicks with the broody hen which incubated them for 19 to 20 days before they hatched. The nest-box is suitable for its purpose

temptation to keep looking into the nest should be resisted. If the chicks are strong, they will emerge cleanly and well.

Germs which cease to develop at the latest stage of the period of incubation give rise to the trouble known as 'dead in shell'. There are several contributory causes and the hen should not be as freely blamed as she often is.

Usual type of slatted-front coop and night cover with additional refinement of a small observation window at the back

Shallow feeding tray is employed for chick food when bantams are being reared under a hover

Nothing can be done to bring these eggs to full maturity and as soon as it is certain that chicks are not 'tapping' inside or chipping their shells, they should be removed.

All that needs to be done, in normal circumstances, is for empty shells to be gently removed for the simple reason that one of them may get over the dome of another shell thus capping it and preventing an otherwise strong chick from hatching.

The hen should be left, with her chicks, for twelve hours after the last one is hatched. She should be taken from the nest at a suitable opportunity for food and water but particularly to relieve her bowels and then left until it is time to remove the chicks to the coop in which they will be reared.

They have sufficient food within them, absorbed from the yolk, for at least 24 hours and will come to no harm by lack of other food.

The rearing coop should be set in a sheltered position and suitably littered with clean, white sawdust. If the weather is inclement some temporary protection should be erected, particularly against driving winds.

Available for the chicks, immediately outside the coop, should be a shallow drinking vessel which contains clean water. It should be of such a pattern that it cannot be overturned by either the hen or chicks and of such a depth that chicks cannot drown in it. A good precaution is to place a piece of brick in the middle of the drinking vessel so that chicks have an 'island' on to which they can scramble; this also acting as a weight to keep the drinker in place.

A shallow feeding trough should also be in place and a supply of small grit is necessary. If chicks are not to have food available to them all the time they will need to be fed every four hours for the first week or two, depending on the variety of bantam being reared and the time of year.

At any rate, the minimum programme will be one feed in the morning, one in the midday period, one in the evening with a late 'extra' at night.

It does not really matter what sort of chick feed is favoured, whether dry meal, mash or prepared chick crumbs, as long as manufactured food which has been specially blended for the job is used. Modern poultry science is such that much of the worry has been taken out of chick rearing by the scientists who work for compounders of poultry foods.

The needs of the broody hen should not be overlooked while she is rearing chicks. It will be necessary to provide her with large corn and a drinking vessel of her own, to which the chicks cannot gain access or she will always be hungry and will rob the chicks of as much of their food as she can reach.

Under normal conditions a broody hen can be expected to remain with her chicks from six to eight weeks, by which time they will be ready to be 'weaned' and treated as growers.

Those who need a greater number of chicks per year or who choose to hatch by incubator because of lack of reliable broody hens, will find any good model will meet their needs. It may be one of the old oil-heated hot-water incubators, a hot-air machine heated in a similar manner or a newer electric incubator.

Whatever is used, the original instructions supplied by the maker should be obtained and carefully followed. The little variations which occur may make all the difference between success and failure.

All incubators have one thing in common; they act best when placed in a room which is free from heavy vibrations and with an equable temperature. It is no use raising the lamp heat to combat severe frost in the hope that the right inside-of-machine heat will be maintained. Far wiser also to place a heater in the room where the machine is to raise the general temperature and leave the machine to run with a normal heat-source, thus maintaining an average of 104°F.

Incubators need an adjustment in respect of bantam eggs, when used to hatch them alone. The inside thermometer should be lowered so that it registers heat at the height from the tray of bantam eggs and not, as would normally be the case, at the position which would be occupied by large fowl eggs.

As with eggs being incubated by broody hens, if bantam eggs are fresh when put into the machine hatching can be expected to take place at least a day earlier than with large fowl.

Adjustments to be made by removing felts etc. as detailed in instructions for use of the incubator concerned can be brought forward one day, especially during clement spring weather. It would be wise to leave removal to normal routine days during late winter or when cold winds are prevalent in early spring.

There is even less need to look at newly hatched chicks in an incubator than with a broody hen. There is almost no risk of eggs becoming 'capped' and those which hatch first go into the drying drawer, where they can be left until the last chicks join them.

If it can be arranged, transfer of chicks from incubator to brooder, where they will be reared, should be carried out at dusk. The chicks will then settle to their new, and slightly cooler home, and not be liable to stray from the source of heat as they might during hours of daylight.

If chicks are to be reared at the bottom of the garden the best method would be the infra-red lamp. All that is needed is a source of electric power, a weatherproof, small house and a temporary surround of hardboard or similar material to form a space into which the chicks will initially be confined.

Before the chicks are transferred from the incubator everything should be got ready for them, the place being clean and littered with clean, white sawdust; drinker and feeding vessel being available as described for natural rearing. The lamp is suspended above the 'compound' into which the chicks will be placed and heat is available long enough for the whole of the area to be warm. That is, the litter and floor should be pleasantly warm so that chicks do not have to crowd together to create warmth on their first arrival.

Warmth at floor level can be tested with the hand and if it is placed on the floor, the amount of warmth on the back of the hand can be judged as to suitability for chicks.

They are placed, one by one, near the centre of the confined area and their behaviour noted after the first hour. If, by this time, they are happily disposed about the compound and 'chirruping' contentedly, then it might be judged that temperature and atmosphere are right. ·

Should chicks commence to huddle together and 'cheep' plaintively, then they are cold and unhappy and the lamp should be lowered until they have sufficient warmth. At the other extreme if the little chicks lay out, panting, with almost no noise they are much overheated and the lamp should be raised to remedy matters.

Better than all the thermometers and set temperatures is observation of the part of the bantam breeder. When chicks are happy, they say so. When miserable, they complain incessantly.

After the bantam chicks are running about freely within their area, the temporary surround may be taken away and the chicks allowed the full use of the small house in which they are being reared. The lamp should be left in the same position, about the middle of the house, so that they gather there to rest and sleep, thus removing any temptation to huddle together in corners.

For the man without the benefit of electricity in his bantam plant, the paraffin heater is efficient. For bantams the 'Putnam' type heater is as good as any because, here again, observation enables one to temper the lamp to the size and age of the chicks until they are finally 'weaned'.

The lamp can be bought and will run for a week with only one filling of oil. The rearer, in which the lamp is situated, can easily be put together.

A box, about 18 in by 3 ft by 9 in deep, but without a top, should be

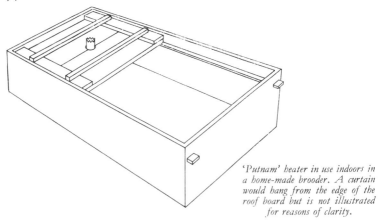

'Putnam' heater in use indoors in a home-made brooder. A curtain would hang from the edge of the roof board but is not illustrated for reasons of clarity.

constructed or obtained. A square of boarding should be made, just large enought to fit inside the box, with a hole bored in the middle large enough for the lamp chimney to pass through.

Slats of wood should be fixed inside the box, along each side and at a height sufficient to allow the body of the rearing lamp to pass underneath the square board, with the chimney protruding. Two opposite sides of the square board should have curtains of hessian or strong cloth nailed to them. These should be just long enough to touch the floor when the board is in position on the slats. Three or four cuts should be made in the curtains to allow chicks to pass in and out.

Broody hen rearing chicks which are completely protected from attack and loss by straying

When the lamp is lighted and the rearing compartment has been warmed for a day, the chicks may be introduced. The square board is then right up to one end of the rearing box. Each week it is brought a little way from the end until, at about six weeks, it is placed centrally.

By this means the warm chamber loses a little of its heat each week and chicks gradually become hardened until they are ready to do without it altogether.

Larger breeds of bantams, such as Sussex and Australorps will be ready to pass from the brooder (or leave the broody hen) from about six weeks of age onwards, according to season of year. Smaller breeds, like Pekins, would require a fortnight longer with some measure of heat at nights.

Accommodation for growing stock may be of many sorts. On the one hand it is necessary to avoid cramped quarters—the coop in which the chicks were reared with the broody hen is not suitable for them in the growing stages. On the other, a house which is much too large and airy can only lead to chicks piling up in the corners at night. Smallest and weakest of them will be crushed and even the stronger ones might go down very quickly with pneumonia, after such treatment.

The cockerel box or ark is usually an efficient unit for chicks during their growing stages. A slatted floor unit is not really a good thing for bantams. They prefer a house with a solid floor and it would be as well to see that there are no dark corners into which they can scramble.

When first weaned the chicks will sleep on the floor. As long as they are happy and healthy they will spread about and continue to grow smoothly. Wrong conditions will result in loss of bodily condition which can soon be noticed by the observant bantam breeder.

Chick food will be replaced by growers' mash and small corn by cut wheat. The number of feeds can be reduced to three daily, giving greenfood at midday. The extra feed at night is still useful, if only to settle the growers into their house.

From about four months of age onwards, when assuming the final feathers of maturity, food should again be changed and extra protein given, especially to heavily feathered varieties.

At this time the sexes should be clearly distinguishable, even to the beginner, and cockerels should be taken away and housed separately. To keep order amongst them, an adult cock which is still in vigorous condition should be run as the 'master'. He will see that any bickering which breaks out to establish mastery is soon quelled.

At this age, perches and droppings boards should be provided in the houses occupied by growers and the bantams induced to perch each night. Some readily take to this form of resting but it is necessary to teach others by lifting them on to the perches after dusk.

Droppings boards should be cleaned down regularly. If houses have nest-boxes for layers they should be covered over so that bantams cannot gain access at this stage in their development.

Although culling for physical defects should be a continuous process from the point of weaning onwards, it now becomes possible to sort the youngsters for outward Standard points in which they need to excel if they are to win prizes in their later lives.

Light breed cockerels soon show a good bit of development in comb and their serrations can clearly be seen and assessed. Any which have bad faults, like fish-tailed spikes, should be removed and disposed of. Bent toes in any breed, other than five toes in breeds which are so adorned, other than four toes in all normally footed breeds, feathers on shanks of clean legged breeds and all similar obvious points should be reasons for culling from the growing flock.

Points of colour begin to emerge as well although these are not yet as certain as the physical defects mentioned above. All the same a Buff bantam with a very black tail or a Black cockerel which immediately reveals white in sickles have no place in the selected stud.

If every bantam is handled, all in one house being done at one time, an assessment of the merits of the stud can soon be made. With rejects withdrawn, and a number of others set aside for sale, the percentage left comes down to a very chosen few indeed.

According to their development and quality they can be selected for exhibition or home breeding stock. The most forward growers which come fit in the late summer season can often be pushed rather quickly to take their place in the showpen before adults are ready or later chicks have developed. If they grow too large, because of the treatment they receive, they will still serve usefully as breeding stock in the earliest pens during the following season.

As long as maturing bantams are not made fat they cannot be fed too well. The high protein mash which is available on the market can usefully be employed to bring certain pullets quickly into lay and prevent them growing too large in body. The early layer never makes the big bodied bird; it is the slow maturer which makes the frame.

Chapter Ten

A PENNING ROOM WILL BE WANTED

To complete the training and conditioning of a bantam intended for show, it is necessary for it to be placed in a showpen of the pattern used at poultry shows. As several birds may need similar treatment at the same time it is best to have a place set aside for the purpose.

This is the penning room where the bantam—and the fancier—both complete their education. The bantam learns deportment and patience with confinement; the owner must have patience to train the bird but learns details of its makeup and temperament in doing so.

If there is a permanent building or cabin which can be converted to use, the penning room may be of any size. It should be snug but adequately ventilated. Weatherproof, draughtproof and ratproof. Not always easy attainments in an old building.

If a new hut is to be provided it will be best to buy one of the Lancashire cabin pattern or have one made to order. Minimum workable size for a normally grown person to move around in is 10 ft by 6 ft, with 6 ft walls rising to a 7 ft 6 in ridge.

There should be ridge ventilation, side hopper windows, a wire door to take the place of the wooden door when it is fastened back during the heat of summer and curtains to shade windows during the same time.

The whole outfit would be best if slightly shaded, rather than in the open and must be away from bantams which are running loose. Birds which are penned should not be in sight of those which are not nor should there be challenging crowing from just outside the door.

The wooden floor should be raised from the ground and wire netting or similar material should be so affixed that neither bantams, dogs, cats nor rats can use the space underneath the house. The floor should be extremely firm so that it does not 'spring' when walked on.

Normal bantam showpens are 1 ft 6 in cube. For a permanent penning room it will be sufficient if showpen fronts are obtained and fitted to home-made divisions.

A shelf, 1 ft 6 in from back to front should be fitted along the back of the house at 2 ft 6 in from the floor. Above this shelf should be built another one, 1 ft 6 in higher. The space for each pen will need 1 ft 6 in frontage.

Allowing for home-made fixings which take up an inch or two of room, 6 pens can be fitted inside a 10 ft long house. Divisions can be of wood and this material is certainly as warm as anything and least liable to condensation. On the other hand it more easily harbours pests and many fanciers now find that sheet asbestos serves best for small jobs of this nature. It is absolutely vermin proof but needs to be drilled before nailing or screwing is attempted.

Below the first shelf there will be a space 1 ft 6 in from the back wall of the house and 2 ft 6 in to the floor. This will be most useful if divided into four conditioning pens, each 2 ft 6 in long. Each should have a front of small mesh netting so that bantams cannot push their heads out and an access door. There should be a perch, a drinker, grit box and feeding vessel. If used for females in lay there should also be a nest-box.

Each of these will serve for one male or a couple of females and will tend to keep birds steady in between shows if they cannot be accommodated in cockerel boxes. When it is intended to show a breeding trio it can be trained in one of these divisions also.

The best material for both the pens beneath and the showpens above is heavy, white sawdust. This should be cleaned out often—not less than once a week. Droppings can readily be taken out nightly when the owner will do most of his work in the penning room.

Wire pens of traditional pattern are still in popular use, but there is a school of thought that these are the cause of frayed neck hackles or twisted hackle, in some cases. Impatient, restive cockerels and pullets are liable to spend much of their time with heads pushed through the wires and constant pressure results in the troubles named.

Some people have, therefore, made their own pen fronts with small, square mesh wire. Others have gone a step further and are experimenting with plastic mesh which can easily be rubbed down but may not be as rigid or durable.

In any case there must be a safe door which the bantam cannot push open by pressure and ease of access for the attendant. Each pen should have a fixed drinker, grit and food vessels.

Penning room to suit
most breeders' needs
(above)

One end of the room can be fitted
with shelves to take appliances
(above)

Although not recommended the
penning room can accommodate a
small rearer out of the show season
(below)

All one side of the penning room
has conditioning quarters on the
ground and two tiers of show pens
above them (above)

It will be found that the partitions tend to gather a film of dust, resulting from movement of the bantams in the pens. This should be wiped down often. Otherwise the day will come when a newly washed bantam will soon look grubby in the home pens—before it even gets to a show.

Also in the penning house should be a corn bin. There must be no 'bucket excitement' as is usual in the outdoor pens. The bantam breeder may not always wish to feed his birds before handling or training them and his arrival should not be heralded by the food bucket. If the bin is made with a flat top it can serve as a seat—necessary when the owner wishes to have control of his bantams for some purpose connected with preparation e.g. cleaning the legs.

A small table or a hinged bench, attached to the front wall, should be available. This is for standing a bantam on to make an examination of its points. If a bench is used it should be capable of being made really rigid. An unsteady bench will unsettle the bantam and undo any good already achieved.

At one end, safely fixed to the wall, there should be a small cabinet in which some of the necessities for showpen attention are kept. Suggested contents are, a sponge, towel, some mild disinfectant suitable for use on the body such as Dettol, Vaseline, Zinc ointment, liver pills, iron tonic pills, Glauber salts, olive oil, cod liver oil capsules, tincture of ferri-perchlor, leg rings, scissors, string, livestock labels, notebook, pencil.

All these are needed either for show preparation or as 'first aid' for those bantams which are noticed to be off colour and are brought to the penning room for convenient treatment before being placed in hospital pens.

Minor ailments are dealt with elsewhere but, briefly, the substances are for cleansing wounds; dressing cuts and scratches; applying to white lobes which are slightly roughened; clearing headpoints which are dull and purplish; toning up pale faced bantams; giving a mild aperient to those with yellowish, frothy droppings; administering to bantams with hard, impacted crops; administering singly to bantams which are not as sleek in plumage and good in body weight as they should be and, finally, the tincture is for dressing wounded combs which are bleeding freely. Any one of these little troubles is liable to crop up at any time and need treatment. None of them are in the nature of serious diseases and bantams so troubled can be brought into the penning room without infecting others.

It is a good thing to have a coat hanger just inside the door where the bantam breeder himself may hang his outer garments in winter time. If he is comfortable when working amongst his birds he will do his job so much better.

It is wise to be on guard that this very useful and attractive shed does not degenerate into something for which it was not intended. It is not the hospital for sick bantams, the place where battery layers are kept or a chick rearing unit.

The penning room should be kept solely for conditioning and training bantams intended for show.

Chapter Eleven

SHOW PREPARATION LEADS TO SUCCESS

Bantams cannot be taken from their runs to a show with reasonable hope of success. They must first be given deportment and bloom which will impress the judge when he is seeking his winners.

Good health is something which must be taken for granted. All prospective winners must be healthy; this is the foundation on which show bloom is built.

The first essential is good condition of body and plumage, also reflected in a glowing headpiece, which must be obtained by careful dieting.

Hard feathered bantams need to be treated in a different manner from those soft-feathered breeds which have a great profusion of plumage. They will have to run out as long as possible and only be brought in to receive showpen training and have their heads and feet well washed and prepared.

Their staple diet will be grain of which good, sound wheat is the best everyday food. A little cracked maize and clipped oats will also be acceptable.

Since these bantams must be muscular and with a high gloss on their plumage they will also need some form of protein. Cracked or broken peas, plain canary seed and hempseed can all be given in small quantities as a change or in addition to the normal grain feed.

As long as they do not become soft and lay on a lot of internal fat it will be found that the hard feathered bantams will also tolerate a certain amount of chopped, lean meat; mash made with linseed jelly; or bread and milk.

Some fanciers prefer to use a conditioner and others give stale sponge cake soaked in sherry or port wine. The whole object is to give the bantams higher feeding than they would normally get to add an ounce or two of flesh and get that glow about them which betokens high condition. They can be 'hardened up' again by running out for a few days, then being brought back into the conditioning pens just before the show.

Soft-feathered bantams need more conditioning, as a rule, principally those breeds with great development of plumage which need a high percentage of protein to maintain feather in good order.

The same end is in view—to provide enough extra nourishment for plumage and for extra body weight so that the birds can stand journeys and confinement at large shows without too much loss of condition.

A bantam which is merely healthy and lean (in normal breeding condition) cannot withstand the rigours of travelling and exhibiting like one that has been properly conditioned.

For the soft-feathered ones, a feeding programme would be based on sound wheat for one feed and a nourishing mash for the other, each day. In addition they would receive an extra which would be any one of chopped, lean meat; soaked biscuit meal with cod liver oil and milk; bread and milk with added sugar; boiled fish; plain canary seed; hempseed; white fish or meat meal fed from a trough; or sponge cake soaked in sherry or port wine. Modern trend is to make use of small

Belgian bantams in showpens are being prepared for show

quantities of prepared, tinned catfood which contains a lot of fish and fishoil for those breeds with rather strong colouring e.g. reds and blacks.

Quantities of food must be tempered to individual needs. Not all breeds need the same amount. Even different bantams of the same breed vary in their requirements.

An old-fashioned but thoroughly well tried system is to give wet mash on three days in the week with the alternative of bread and milk on two days and additional protein, say, meat and linseed jelly on each of the other days. The great thing is to ring the changes so that appetites do not become stale.

To make bread and milk so that it is thoroughly appetising and not a soggy mess, stale bread should be rusked in a slow oven. It is then broken into pieces of suitable size and stored in an airtight tin. Sufficient for one feed is soaked in cold water until thoroughly swollen. Surplus water is drained off, the soaked rusk squeezed and whole milk added until thoroughly absorbed. A little sugar is added.

The linseed jelly mentioned above is prepared from whole seed (not linseed meal). A handful is put into a pan and covered with cold water. It is then simmered over slow heat until the seeds become rather soft. When set to cool, the result is a jelly-like mass. This is used, in moderate quantities, to moisten meal to make a wet mash. Too liberal use will create results as though a laxative had been used.

The bantam fancier who is away from home all day and cannot make arrangements to have any of these supplementary feeds used as the evening meal should see that the quantities normally used in the afternoon are reduced and give the supplementary late at night, by artificial light. This will be suitable for individual bantams but will preclude general conditioning of small groups unless artificial lighting can be arranged for their houses.

Accommodation for bantams being got ready for show is as important as feeding. All males, on arriving at the point of maturity when bickering starts, must be housed singly. The best accommodation is what is known as a cockerel box and can be made to any size and pattern appropriate to the breed. Essential requirements of perch, drinker, feeding vessel, dry floor and roof and proper ventilation should be provided.

Females can be run together in small groups. Three or four are very manageable and thrive better; they seem to need company where the males need isolation. It is best if their houses are not set to face the cockerel boxes of the males.

It is economical and wise to sort out the birds for quality and breed points before grouping them for conditioning. It will save quite an amount of rather expensive food, as well as room and labour.

Instead of thinking of brightness in headpoints and general vitality as deriving from some bottle of tonic, the thought should be firm that much of this can be had free by ensuring a supply of fresh greenfood, chopped finely, for each bantam every day.

After the birds have settled into their conditioning quarters it will be possible to assess them better than when they were on the open

Shaded from the direct rays of the sun yet enjoying maximum fresh air this Millefleur d'Uccles hen will be in peak form when exhibited

run. Details will become more apparent and the best of them should now be taken into the penning room for training.

A bantam should first be put into a showpen late at night so that it settles there during darkness. Most of them will be rather wild and nervous, crouching and carrying themselves badly.

For the first day, feed them but leave them alone. They are not yet ready to handle. Commencing on the second day, preferably at night under artificial light, much can be done to quieten a bantam by gently stroking its wattles and then transferring the judging stick or light cane to its back and passing it gently from shoulders to saddle.

Within a very short time, if confidence is established and the bantam learns to associate the owner's visit with a titbit such as a little canary seed, it will tolerate a hand being put into its pen without rushing wildly round. It can then be caressed and induced to stand properly to show off the points of the breed. A Pekin, for example, will be disturbed as little as possible while a Modern Game will be encouraged to stretch to the top of the pen. A titbit of food held in the fingers helps matters along here.

Immersed in soap suds but so very clean and attractive when rinsed and dried

Every owner should know the salient points of his breed and adjust training methods accordingly.

As soon as a bantam has learned deportment it should be returned to the small house from which it was taken for conditioning to continue. It should not be kept in a showpen within the penning house or it will become stale.

Being trained, it will soon accept penning when a show is immediately in view. This is especially so in the case of the light coloured breeds which must be washed for success in the showpen.

Washing is quite legitimate preparation when designed only to restore bantams which have become soiled by domestic conditions to the pristine cleanliness that would be theirs in state of nature. It does not include bleaching or colour washing (dyeing).

A good bath will make a bantam look and feel better. It will help plumage to lie correctly. There are several different ways in which birds can be prepared for show but, if the following notes are closely followed, the final result will be satisfactory. Bantam fanciers may devise their own methods of heating for the drying process or make special 'drying boxes' employing electric heating etc. On the other hand, they may choose to follow the traditional method outlined.

Equipment required is one bath of suitable size for the breed concerned; this will hold warm washing water. A second bath is needed for rinsing water and a third for a final rinse. In the case of white plumaged bantams a touch of washday blue should be added to the final water. Also needed are two or three good, absorbent towels, a large sponge of good quality, a small sponge, good nailbrush and a jug or other means of ladling water.

White soap flakes and white toilet soap are also needed, but washing powders or liquid detergents should not be used until their action has been tried on a bantam not intended for show and they have been proved harmless to feathers and skin.

There should be a good supply of hot water and access to a cold tap, where the washing is to take place.

Take the bantam to be bathed under the left arm and restrain any movement of its wings by gentle pressure from the elbow, holding the bantam to the side of the body. Its head is free and shanks may be grasped by the operator's hand and held forward.

A preliminary sponge down will remove superficial dirt from legs and feet. The nailbrush is well wetted and thoroughly soaped and the shanks and feet are scrubbed, both backs and fronts. Cleansing the legs and feet should be carried out away from the bath so that the water is not sullied. They are rinsed clean.

The bantam is now stood in the bath, facing the operator, and its wings held down by the thumbs, the hands passing over its wings and the fingers restraining the thighs. The whole of the plumage is well wetted with the very warm water in which soap flakes have been dissolved.

As the bird gets wetter it will become more tractable and quite easy to manage. Care should be taken to wet thoroughly under the wings, in the roots of the neck and saddle hackles, and at the base of the tail, as well as all the wing feathers. The large sponge should be used firmly but not harshly on all parts of the plumage to remove any surface dirt, and ensure that plumage is soaked.

The small sponge is wetted and soaped lightly with toilet soap then all headpoints, comb, face etc. should be gently cleansed and immediately rinsed. Lightly rub them over with the small sponge damped with clean, cold water and the bantam will feel more comfortable. While this has been going on the plumage of the body has had time to get thoroughly wet through.

With the large sponge heavy with soapy water start at the top of the head and work down the neck, finishing at the shoulders. Then from the top of the breast, down to the point of the breast bone. With the 'front' done, the operator now can concentrate on the body.

The tracts to be washed are the back, from shoulders to tail roots, the upper side of the wings, the main flight feathers, under the wings, the underpart of the body, thighs and tail. If badly soiled, feathers can be lightly scrubbed with the nailbrush down and across but not from the tip upwards. It is better to 'squeegee' plumage between the fingers and thumb as hard scrubbing can leave telltale patches on the surface of the plumage.

When clean, the bantam should be lifted from the bath and surplus lather swept off the plumage. It is then put into the second bath, only a few degrees cooler than the first, and the parts are rinsed in the same order with the object of getting out soap which was previously worked in. A third transfer to the final bath which contains clean, lukewarm water and the washing is completed.

As much water as possible should be mopped out of the feathers with the large sponge (rinsed and squeezed out) and more drying done with a towel. Wrapped in another, dry towel, the bantam can now be laid across the operator's knee to have the edges of the scales of its legs and feet manicured and dirt removed from under the scales.

When light-coloured birds, such as buffs and blues, must be washed the first bath water should not be as hot as for whites nor must blue be added to the final rinse.

Ordinary exhibition baskets, in clean condition and with white sawdust or straw on the bottom, should receive the washed and manicured bantams and be placed before a brisk fire to enable the birds to dry evenly and fairly quickly.

As soon as reasonably dry the birds should be taken back to the penning room and penned alone, clean sawdust having been put in the pens.

It is the fashion for Modern and Old English Game males to be dubbed for show, and this should be regarded as an essential point of preparation. Cockerels are dubbed after their main plumage has grown and their sickle feathers are fully developed. Modern Game have their combs cut off more closely than Old English, giving the desired 'snaky' appearance.

Except for cutting more closely to the head in Moderns the method is the same for both breeds or, indeed, for any bird which needs to be dubbed e.g. a Leghorn needed to run out in the breeding pen which would be better without his large comb.

An assistant should hold the bantam concerned and face the operator. He should hold the bird's legs and wings firmly so that it does not struggle free at a critical moment. The operator should proceed with confidence.

He must have a pair of strong, sharp scissors with curved blades. These can be bought for the job in hand from veterinary suppliers. Each cut must be made from the back of the head to the front and not from front to back. Each earlobe is first removed with a single cut. The wattles then follow in similar manner.

The operator then takes the lower mandible of the bird's beak between the fingers and thumb of one hand and gently stretches the bantam cockerel's neck to its full extent. With the other hand manipulating the scissors he then removes the comb with a single sweeping cut at the height desired for the breed concerned.

The head is then swabbed with cold water and it will generally suffice for the bantam to be returned to the run from which he came. The following day a little plain Vaseline may be rubbed over the cut parts. This will prevent scarring. Scabs will form and should come away to leave a clean job within ten to fourteen days.

Should any bantam be encountered with a particularly thick base to its comb, causing additional bleeding, a few wisps of sterilised gauze or cottonwool may be placed over the cut. These will come away when the wound heals.

Although not strictly a part of show conditioning for bantams of all ages the moult does affect those which are a year or more old and can most conveniently be dealt with here.

Bantams moult in the summer and autumn in order to grow new plumage, resilient and weatherproof, to serve them throughout winter and the following breeding season.

From the point of view of prizewinning it is as well to realise that feathers spring from certain well defined tracts and are not placed haphazardly over the body. A plucked carcase should be studied to appreciate this.

If left to moult in their own way most bantams will grow their new plumage in such a way that it is not evenly enough developed for show purposes. Usually, a helping hand is needed.

Birds which have been shown and are in high condition should be run down until they are lean. When their feathers look sufficiently 'ripe' for the moult the bantams should be confined to their houses and food cut down to the bare minimum. Water should still be supplied and a little greenfood would help. But corn and mash must be very sparingly given.

Feathers should start to drop freely within a week. Large stiff feathers, and leg feather and crests in those breeds so adorned, may need to be removed by hand, especially if well worn. New plumage will then come through smooth and even in place of the feathers which have been removed. If left to Nature some footings and crests will not be wholly renewed.

In obstinate cases where body plumage does not begin to drop freely a complete bath and a quick, hot drying will often achieve what is wanted. In any case the bantam will benefit from the cleanliness thus achieved.

Soon after the old feathers have dropped, new ones will be seen encased in their sheaths, giving bantams a porcupine-like appearance. At this stage they should not be handled but the amount of protein can be stepped up, as when birds are being conditioned for show. This will enable sound, new plumage to develop.

Food should now be given in full measure. Full bodily condition is needed if feathers are to grow well. Not always appreciated is the fact that scales on legs are also subject to an annual moult. Old, brittle scales fall away and new, soft ones replace them. The old scales can be helped by pressure on their sides from the thumb nail, revealing smooth, fully-coloured scales underneath. A little care and practice will soon enable the exhibitor to have his old birds with legs as good as his young stock.

The moult is a perfectly natural process and applies to all adult bantams, whether wanted for exhibition or not. Special care is only needed for showbirds. All breeding stock can be allowed to run in the usual way and will drop their feathers and grow new ones in normal course—but the final result may not be as smooth and even as is wanted for the showpen.

Chapter Twelve

THE AIM ACHIEVED—SHOWDAY

All that has been done in the way of breeding, rearing and show preparation undergoes the acid test as showday approaches. Nothing should now be neglected that will add to the chance of the chosen bantam arriving at the show fit and fresh, and being afterwards carefully looked after to maintain it for another event.

Different breeds need different amounts of space in exhibition hampers and adjustments should be made to accommodate them properly. It is obvious that a Japanese with its massive tail will need more room than a slim Modern Game. Many other breeds differ considerably, although the contrast is not so stark.

As a general rule it is wise to arrange bantams so that males and females alternate in the compartments of travelling baskets. Weather conditions should be considered and while a normal hamper will serve during the summer the same basket may need to be made more weatherproof by adding a layer of stout brown paper during winter weather. In thinking of the uses of polythene sheet as a weatherproof medium for basket lids, it should also be remembered that this material does not allow air to pass through it. This means that there must be proper ventilation if baskets are to be covered with this type of material.

Exhibitors who rely on rail transit for their bantams to and from shows should make themselves conversant with British Rail bye-laws and statutory regulations, which may be seen on request at any station. These limit the amount of compensation payable in case of loss— something which ought to be more widely known.

On arrival at the show the exhibitor will find that stewards are busy

(Left) General layout of an all-bantam show with judging in progress

(Right) A judge, attended by his steward, assesses the merits of an exhibit

penning rail-borne bantams and there is a general air of 'organised confusion' to get ready for the time stated for judging.

He should set his own baskets in some corner and check the numbered pens which have been provided for his bantams. It is always wise, when benching a number of white or light coloured birds, to wipe down the sides of the pens with a large duster. Litter on the pen floors should be checked to see that it is adequate. If not, a word to the chief steward will usually bring what is wanted.

The exhibitor is not at liberty to provide his own bedding nor to add anything which will distinguish his bantam from any other. If numbered leg rings have been provided by the show authorities he should see that each bird has the ring bearing the proper number for its class. No other rings, except the sealed rings of The Poultry Club or some breed society, may be worn.

With the pens ready each bird should be unbasketed and looked over for any slight soiling which may have occurred on the journey. With a clean towel wrapped round its body the bantam is tucked under one arm, head forward, and its headpoints lightly rubbed over with a small sponge moistened with head dressing. The sole object is to remove travel weariness and freshen up the bird. This is not illegitimate preparation.

A good head dressing is colourless and slightly astringent causing that fresh look which judges like. A reliable dressing can be made up by any chemist and contains 2 oz spirits of wine; 1 oz camphorated oil; 1 oz glycerine; $\frac{1}{4}$ oz citric acid. This should be well mixed and applied sparingly.

The prepared bantam is gently placed in its pen, head forward, and stood squarely on its feet. It should be seen that its wings and tail are displayed in proper order and not disarranged.

A very small amount of some favourite food, such as canary seed, should be given to 'settle' the bantam in. It should be gently posed and spoken to—and left for the judge's attention.

Having been handled by the judge and possibly inspected a second time if in the running for high honours, then moved round the pen by innumerable judging sticks, the bantam must be rather weary at the end of a show.

Additionally it has been closely penned and a rather warm atmosphere has prevailed (tents and halls alike have a remarkable way of becoming unbearably warm during the afternoon). Feed may have been scanty or too generous. In any case it will not have been of the usual sort.

First thing, on returning home is to put each bantam in its showpen in the penning house and give it a nourishing, light feed such as bread and milk.

As soon as possible each bantam should have its head and feet washed in a solution of disinfectant and the fluff surrounding the vent cleansed, if this is needed.

With these precautions taken it will soon show no ill effects from its outing and should be removed from the penning room into the cockerel box or other accommodation previously occupied.

When resting between shows bantams should not be allowed to become soiled unnecessarily but should be allowed the fresh air treatment which a cockerel box gives, so that they remain fit and healthy. They should, however, be shaded from the direct rays of the sun and weather at all times, or plumage will become sunburned and stained.

If feeding is adjusted to the needs of each bird, it will take about three days in a training pen and, perhaps, a bath to bring it to another 'peak' for further exhibition.

Chapter Thirteen

A BREED FOR ANY PURPOSE

There can be no doubt that bantams offer a more comprehensive selection of form, colour and plumage than is found among large poultry. The reason is that every known large breed that is worth bantamising has been so treated while there are, additionally, bantam breeds which have no large counterparts.

It is possible to divide and sub-divide the miniature breeds and true bantams in several ways but few of these divisions give a real clue as to the purpose for which the bantams exist or the qualities that may be expected of them.

Some indication of their merits is given in Chapter 16, which describes the known breeds in alphabetical order. It will generally be found that classes are provided at shows for separate breeds and the remainder compete in classes for Other Varieties. It is rare, nowadays, for a class to be provided for 'Game' or 'Hard-Feather' while another is for 'Feathered-legged' or 'Soft-feather'. Much more usual is to find the popular breeds with their own classes and the others together in the last class in the show.

With this in mind, the new breeder should take care to find out what any breed which attracts by reason of form or colour is like to breed and exhibit. What is more, he should learn whether it is hardy and reasonably easy to handle and what return may be expected in the way of eggs or whether spare cockerels provide a little meat for the home table.

Within reason, all the miniatures which represent large breeds of 'heavy' classification will lay reasonably well and their eggs will have tinted or brown shells. Those who are interested in showing eggs as well as birds will find Sussex will lay tinted eggs which will win prizes and Marans lay eggs with dark brown shells which invariably do well. Other reliable layers of tinted eggs are Buff Plymouth Rocks and Rhode Island Reds. Some of the Wyandottes, notably Columbian and Laced, are also creditable layers. Australorps have a goodish reputation in this respect also.

Miniatures of Mediterranean light breeds, such as Anconas, Leghorns and Minorcas will lay white-shelled eggs of good shape and matt finish which will be likely to win prizes in their classes. Hamburghs also lay white eggs which are rather rounder in shape and often glossy.

As the exception which disproves the rule, the Welsummer bantam (which is also a light breed) lays beautifully shaped eggs of good size which have deep brown colouring and matt finish.

Small table birds will result when Ixworths, Indian Game, Jubilee Indian Game and Buff Orpingtons are bred. All of them have substantial bodies and the Indians are particularly wide across the breast with heavy thighs.

It is unusual to find anyone with a primary interest in bantam table fowl, but the sideline, which surplus cockerels may give, should not be overlooked.

None of the smaller bantams, whether miniatures as in Old English and Modern Game, or true bantams without a large counterpart as Sebrights and Rosecombs, make any pretensions of high laying or table-bird abilities. They are primarily kept for their attractiveness and beauty. The females lay eggs in the normal spring season and while they may be relatively small they are laid with a good degree of regularity during the breeding season and produce well-formed, strong chicks.

The Poultry Club, which incorporates The British Bantam Association, and is the ruling body for Standard-bred poultry and the conduct of shows for them, lays down regulations in respect of several points. These are, a definition of Game as opposed to Hard Feather. Classification of all breeds as Light or Heavy, the guiding light here being body weight set down in Breed Standards. Listing those bantam breeds which are regarded as Ornamental.

Game bantams, where so described without any other qualification, include Modern and Old English Game only. All other breeds with Hard feather, such as Indian Game, Malays, Aseels or Sumatras may not be exhibited in classes which define Game only. They must then by shown as Any Other Variety exhibits.

The Poultry Club does not admit of birds of Intermediate weight in its classifications. All are either Light or Heavy breeds. Bantams follow their large counterparts in this respect.

Heavy Breeds are:

Australorp
Barnevelder
Brahma
Cochin
* Creve Coeur
Croad Langshan
Dorking
* Essex
Faverolle
Frizzle
Indian Game
Ixworth
* Jersey Giant
Jubilee Indian Game
* La Fleche
* Langshan
Malay

* Malines
Marans
* Marsh Daisy
Modern Game
* Modern Langshan
* New Hampshire Red
* Norfolk Grey
* North Holland Blue
* Orloff
Orpington
Plymouth Rock
Rhode Island Red
* Surrey
Sussex
* Wherwell
Wyandotte

Light Breeds are:

Ancona
Andalusian
Aseel
* Bresse
Campine
* Coveney White
Hamburgh
Houdan
* Lakenfelder
Leghorn
Minorca
Old English Game
* Old English Pheasant Fowl
Phoenix

Poland
* Redcap
Scots Dumpy
Scots Grey
* Sicilian Buttercup
* Sicilian Flower Bird
* Silkie
* Spanish
* Sultan
Sumatra Game
Welsummer
* Wyndham Black
Yokohama

* Breeds that have either never been bred in bantam form or are not known in Great Britain today.

The Poultry Club defines an ornamental bantam as having some additional feature or form of plumage which merit it being considered highly decorative or elaborate as compared with bantams of straightforward make and shape.

CHARACTERISTICS OF BREEDS OF BANTAMS

Bantam Breed	Ornamental	Miniature of Large Breed	Hard Feathered	Soft Feathered	Natural Bantam	Utility Breed
Ancona	–	*	–	*	–	*
Andalusian	–	*	–	*	–	–
Australorp	–	*	–	*	–	*
Barnevelder	–	*	–	*	–	*
Barbus d'Anvers	*	–	–	*	*	–
Barbus d'Uccles	*	–	–	*	*	–
Booted	*	–	–	*	*	–
Brahma	*	*	–	*	–	–
Cochin or Pekin	*	–	–	*	*	–
Creve Coeur	*	*	–	*	–	–
Croad Langshan	–	*	–	*	–	*
Dorking	–	*	–	*	–	–
Faverolle	–	*	–	*	–	*
Frizzle	*	–	–	*	*	–
Hamburgh	–	*	–	*	–	*
Houdan	*	*	–	*	–	–
Indian Game	–	*	*	–	–	*
Ixworth	–	*	–	*	–	*
Japanese	*	–	–	*	*	–
Jubilee Indian Game	–	*	*	–	–	*
Leghorn	–	*	–	*	–	*
Malay	–	*	*	–	–	–
Marans	–	*	–	*	–	*
Minorca	–	*	–	*	–	*
Modern Game	–	*	*	–	–	–
Nankin	–	–	–	*	*	–
Old English Game	–	*	*	–	–	–
Orpington	–	*	–	*	–	–
Phoenix	–	*	–	*	–	–
Plymouth Rock	–	*	–	*	–	*
Poland	*	*	–	*	–	–
Redcap	–	*	–	*	–	–
Rhode Island Red	–	*	–	*	–	*
Rosecomb	*	–	–	*	*	–
Rumpless	–	*	*	*	–	–
Scots Dumpy	–	*	–	*	–	–
Scots Grey	–	*	–	*	–	–
Sebright	*	–	–	*	*	–
Sumatra	–	*	*	–	–	–
Sussex	–	*	–	*	–	*
Welsummer	–	*	–	*	–	*
Wyandotte	–	*	–	*	–	*
Yokohama	*	*	–	*	–	–

The list comprises:

Barbus d'Anvers	Houdan
Barbus d'Uccles	Japanese
Booted	Pekin
Brahma	Poland
Creve Coeur	Rosecomb
Frizzle	Sebright

Yokohama, and such others as may be approved in future.

Although Booted and Creve Coeur are listed they are not actually in existence at the time of writing. The former are extant on the Continent under the name of Sabelpoot and may be re-introduced here when regulations permit. The latter are the subject of minor interest and may be re-made by an enthusiast. It was, therefore, necessary to make provision for them in the list recently issued.

Bearing in mind that all bantams are, more or less, intended for exhibition the Table on p. 78 has been compiled to summarise the qualities inherent in the various breeds. Where bantams are shown as having 'utility' properties this is merely an indication that they are likely to have some useful return to offer in the way of eggs or meat; it does not imply that miniatures will be equally as good as large breeds in the laying shed.

The entry in respect of Rumpless needs a word of explanation. Although usually derived from Old English Game the fact is that any bantam naturally without a caudal appendage (and feathered-tail) could be shown as Rumpless, regardless of general appearance. It might just as well originate from soft-feathered as from Game bantams.

Chapter Fourteen

GUIDE TO COLOUR BREEDING

White bantams are popular in many breeds. Their plumage should be of one, pure shade throughout. Commonest faults are discoloured tops in males, either 'brassiness' which is congenital or 'weathering' which is caused by exposure to the elements. The two should not be confused.

Brassiness will always show up as a yellow tinge in hackle and back feathers on males, whether they are sheltered from the weather or not. Weathering is the equivalent of the tan which we gain from an open-air life and derives from the same conditions. A weathered bantam, when moulted, can be kept indoors and remain quite white. In the two foregoing conditions discolouration is confined to the upper surface of the plumage, underfluff being quite white.

Brassy tops in males constitute a sex-limited factor. Sisters to the badly coloured males carry the factor and will pass it on to their sons. Remedy is to find a stay-white male and use him and all his female relatives in the breeding pens. When a family of males with very brassy top colour makes its appearance, all the female relatives of these cocks should be discarded, even if the intention is to mate them to a stay-white male. 'Sappiness' occurs in young stock which has just reached the point of maturity and shows as a cream tinge coming from the base of the feather upwards. Fluff is just as evenly discoloured as the rest of the plumage. This tinge of cream usually clears upon full maturity being attained and after bantams have run out for a week or two or, in the case of exhibition specimens, had their first complete bath. Yellow-skinned and legged white bantams such as Leghorns are generally more sappy than those with white skins, such as Sussex.

Very small, black tickings are often found on the spur feathers of the wings and the tail coverts of bantams which are otherwise impeccably white. As long as these are strictly under control and not widely spread throughout the plumage such bantams may safely be used in the breeding pen.

All-black breeds such as Australorps and Minorcas are those in which the plumage, eyes, legs and feet are all dark. This compatible colouring ensures that the majority of the bantams are sound in undercolour—an important point in blacks. If they are not, they should be for rejection.

Bantams which show grey in flight or white in tail should not be used for an all-black breeding pen. Others which are faulty in eye colour or with pale shanks should also be culled.

It is possible to breed sound, black bantams which fail because they are dull in colour or have purple sheen, when they should have green lights in their plumage. This is a point for constant selection; a nice 'soft' colour with plenty of sheen being the ideal.

All-blacks usually produce some birds (particularly cockerels) with small amounts of yellow (brass) or flashes of red in their plumage. This colouring is most readily seen in the neck hackle and on the shoulders of the cockerel so affected. If used in moderation in the breeding pen, some brightening of colour may result. A warning is given that to use such males repeatedly must result in the defect being intensified and fixed within the stud.

Blue plumage is non-existent in bantams. What is usually described as blue is, in actual fact, dilute black. The exact shade desired by the Standard should be known and aimed for. Unless otherwise specified, blue plumage should be all of one shade without hard edges to the feathers. Some breeds, notably Andalusians and Orpingtons, should have a dark lacing round each feather.

Most blue breeds throw a number of chicks which are almost or wholly black (dark) and some which are splashed or wholly white (light), as well as others which approximate to the ideal colour.

Both are valuable to balance colour in the breeding pen the darks being used on the female side and mated to a cockerel which is clear but rather pale in his shade of blue. Lights can be used to counterbalance dull, dark blue in the same way. In an extreme case, a light cockerel could be mated with dark pullets and a percentage of exhibition blues would be expected amongst their progeny.

Safest method is to mate blue to blue, balancing depth of colour as required and bringing in darks and lights as indicated. Classic case of Mendelism is always quoted for Blue Andalusians. When Blues are mated to Blues the offspring gives 25% darks, 50% blues, and 25% lights. When lights and darks are mated together the offspring is 100% blue; but they may not be of exhibition shade, which can only be ensured by using show-quality stock in the breeding pen.

Particular care should be taken that males have little or no red feather in their make-up and wings of both sexes are sound.

Barred and Cuckoo bantams, of which examples are Barred Plymouth Rocks and Scots Greys, may originally have come from black/white matings which also gave early blues. They have been segregated for so long that it would be folly to try to gain points by re-introducing black or white blood from which they sprang.

Barred plumage should always start with a dark tip and the even, transverse markings must be as regular as possible, going well down the feather. Undercolour should be confined to a small area and not allowed to encroach on the feather proper where the markings should be clear and well defined.

Brassy hackles and red shoulders should be kept within strict limits in the males and barred should be mated with barred in the breeding pens, those of slightly light shade being mated with those which are a little dark. Medium barreds of the proper showpen quality should be mated together.

All-black pullets are sometimes produced and they can be used on the female side of the breeding pen if the general colour of the stud is becoming too light. They should only be blacks bred at first generation from barreds and must be mated with a very clearly marked male.

Cuckoo markings are less well defined than barrings and there are fewer markings to the feather. Definition between bars and ground colour is not as sharp but the same general principles apply. Undercolour should always be carefully watched as it is easy to get it too light in this colouring with the result that all males are bred with white in tail and some with white in flights.

Mottled breeds such as Belgians and Pekins are identical with so-called Spangleds, as in Wyandottes. Anconas are of the same basic pattern except that their standard defines the shape of the white marking which should occur on each feather.

Colour, in this group, is a black feather with a white tip at the end. In Anconas it should be shaped like the letter V; other breeds may be less precisely marked but the white should be regularly and evenly distributed over the plumage.

Problems relate to undercolour, which can easily become too light. because of the amount of white in plumage, thus causing grey wings and tails, and clarity of white tippings.

When very clear tippings are obtained undercolour is likely to be light. When undercolour is dark enough to ensure soundness in body plumage, tippings are likely to be rather greyish.

These two are the main points to take into consideration when mating the breeding pen, balance being sought. It is likely that a breeding pen will contain bantams which are too light and too dark in colouring, as well as some which are just about right.

Resultant chicks will fall into three similar groups and it may be found that the light coloured ones will be fit to show when just attaining maturity; the middle group will be the main exhibition birds in their first year and the dark coloured ones, which have small amounts of white in their first year, may moult out into winning adults.

As in all breeds with black in their plumage, red or brass in hackle and shoulders is very likely to occur in males and must be carefully restrained. It is generally contended that to use a little of it in the breeding pen will result in ground colour which has wonderful sheen, just as necessary here as in all-blacks.

Black and white pattern of plumage, consisting of black striping in neck hackles, black tails and black markings in wings associated with white body plumage has always been popular. First seen in Light Brahmas, then popular in Columbian Wyandottes this pattern is now excellent in Light Sussex. It is usually referred to as 'Columbian' plumage.

Body colour should be white throughout and as pure as possible underneath. Some slight smokiness is often visible in underfluff and Columbian Wyandottes are standardised as having this undercolour. What is undesirable is ticking or patches of black in undercolour and outcrops of black in top colour, associated with striped saddles in males.

Black should be confined to a stripe down the centre of each neck hackle feather, this being wholly contained by an even edging of white. The stripe should be free from shaftiness and should carry a green sheen. Common faults are 'double-lacing' when each feather bears a shadowy edge of black on the outer rim and 'run through' hackles when the black continues to the end of the feather and is not contained by the white edge. If a male with a double-laced hackle is used at the head of a breeding pen it is quite likely that many of his female offspring will have run through hackles.

Tails should be black, except that the top pair of feathers in the females' tails may be laced with white and tail coverts should be black, laced with white. It is often difficult to get hens with tails which are quite black, many being grey in the upper part of the main feathers and tail coverts. Similarly, males may fail by being white at the roots of the sickles.

Similar faults should be avoided on both sides of the breeding pen, hens which are sound in tail (even if somewhat dull in colour) being preferred if a male has much white in sickle feathers. With a thoroughly sound-tailed male something can be given away in tail colour in hens if pure body colour is thus attained.

When impure colour has to be used on one side of the pen it is usually preferred in the female, the male being absolutely clear on top. In hackles, hens with run-through striping can often be used in the breeding pen if mated with a male with perfect lacing around his striping.

Wings should be marked on the inner edge of each feather with black, so that the closed wing shows white. This is regarded as a good reservoir of pigment and birds with grey or lightly marked wings should not be mated together. Lack of pigment in wings is usually associated with very pure white but points would be lost in the show-pen by birds which were much deficient at this point.

Males may have brassy tops in the same way as whites and should be treated in the same way. There is also a tendency for some strains to throw males which have sandy patches on their shoulders. This fault can be eradicated in the same way as brassy tops and should be regarded as equally serious.

Buff bantams have always commanded a good following. Once the shade demanded by the Standard or dictated by fashion has been appreciated for a particular breed (the Pekin is vastly different in depth of colour from the Plymouth Rock, for instance) all breeds can be produced to the same formula of mating.

In Buffs pigment should be of one colour only. All parts of the plumage should be level and one section of feathering should match any other. Undercolour should harmonise with top colour and pigment should be carried well down to the skin, fluff being a shade of buff.

Places where there is likely to be weakness are the main tail feathers which may be either rather shafty and grizzled in colour, through lack of pigment, or have some smudges of black or bronze in tail through too much. Wings are liable to be weak in colour when the shafts are light and the web of the feather is pale or there may be dark, minute pepperings in birds of 'hot' colouring.

No matter what shade of colour he is the sire for a good Buff breeding pen must be absolutely level throughout. His neck hackle should flow on to his shoulders in such a way that it matches them and they, in turn, should accord with wings and back. The back should lead to the saddle hackle which, again, should be of one even shade.

White at roots of neck hackle, under the saddle or in the sickle feathers will result in washy coloured offspring. Soundness is essential.

His mates will also be level in colouring throughout and a key to suitability is if the breast colour of the cock matches with colour of back of the hens.

Female plumage (and the breast of the male) should be free from light coloured shafts or hard, shiny edges. Female hackles should not be hard and shiny, although this point is difficult to get right.

In spite of many opinions to the contrary the one safe way to breed Buffs is by mating a male of exhibition colour to hens of the same quality. If circumstances dictate that this is not possible then extra colour should be in the underfluff of the females and sweet, level top colouring should be on the male.

Red, as exemplified in Rhode Island Reds and Red Sussex, was once the bedfellow of Buff. In very early days both these colours derived from the same sources. By allowing some black pigment to be associated with a deeper colour, red (as now known) evolved.

To be successful in the showpen a deep shade, more chocolate than red, is necessary.

Keeping in mind all the points of level colour and freedom from hard edges causing lacing, set out for Buffs, one or two additional qualifications are necessary for good breeding birds in Rhode Island Reds. They must have pure undercolour, free from black or white. Males should have no black markings in neck hackle but pullets have black ticking. Both have black tails and black markings in their wings, which show all red when normally closed.

Red Sussex have bluish undercolour and the same black markings as described under notes relating to Columbian colouring. They try to combine two colours and do it fairly successfully.

Worst trouble in either breed is that if colour is dark and black points are intense there is likely to be an outcrop of black on the wings or (in some cases) at the edge of the breast feathering.

Attempt must be made to balance faults with virtues and if a pen of all exhibition bantams could be mated, the results would justify it. It is essential to have depth of undercolour in Rhode Island Reds allied with level top colour. Males with ginger hackles will breed pullets which are unlevel in colour.

Black-red is a natural pattern in which the males and females are compatible, winners in both sexes being bred from the same parents. Best example is, probably, the Welsummer where the black parts of the male are somewhat tinged with red and the females have some ruddiness about their colouring instead of the soft salmon breasts which are demanded where double-mating is in vogue e.g. Brown Leghorns.

In Old English Game it has long been fashionable to demand exhibition cocks with very bright top colour, resulting in the rather darker Partridge-bred birds being discarded in favour of those bred from Wheaten coloured hens.

Main point is to get the cock right, with sound black parts and bright hackles, free from striping. Shoulders and back should be good, solid red and the wing bay should also be solid in colour. Although he may be bred to hens which are rather hard and marbled in colour to breed good cockerels, the hens which are shown are soft, wheaten colour and are, as likely as not, bred from a male which is rather too much marked with red in his black. This is a modified form of double-mating which most people get over by using a good, average cock to hens of both hues.

The true partridge-bred Black-red cock will be darker on top and may have some striping in his hackles. His mates will be soft brown, stippled finely with black. Within reason, all their offspring will be of the same constant pattern.

Standard points for each Black-red variety should be known and aimed for. In Modern Game the males must not be striped in hackle and the females should have softly coloured salmon breasts, shading down to ash grey thighs. Body colour should be soft brown with very fine black stippling and golden shading. These artificial requirements indicate double-mating for colour and this used to be the case.

Today, it is more usual to breed a 'balanced' pen and males may not be as bright on top as they once were nor females as soft in colour. It is considered more acceptable to make allowances than to burden the breed with double-mating.

Piles, derive directly from Black-reds and may be interbred with them. The difference is that where the Black-red is black the Pile is white in the males. In females hackle and breast colouring of the Black-red occurs on a white body. Piles are mated with Piles while colouring is sound but as soon as there is any sign of fading, particularly on wing bays, a Black-red cross is made. This may not be entirely successful in the first generation but the crossed birds should be bred back to Piles the following year, when better results should be obtained.

Duckwings also derive from Black-reds and may be interbred. In their case the red is diluted to cream hackles and orange shoulders in males and the black retained. Females are of the same pattern of markings as Black-reds except that their breasts are a shade lighter and silvery-grey replaces the soft brown of the Black-red body colour.

In all cases there is a tendency for females to have too much colouring on their wings. This results in foxy sided Black-reds and rusty Duckwings, as well as rosewinged Piles. A little of this in the breeding pen will help retain colour in cockerels but is undesirable in the showpen. When body colour is pure and soft in colour, breasts may not be as intense in hue as is desired. As in so many other cases where doublemating is not employed, the happy medium should be aimed for in the breeding pen in the expectation that both sorts will again occur in offspring.

Males with poor wing bays which are not of the correct colouring, which run short and end with black or which break with black or white, as the case may be, are likely to lose points in the showpen and are of little use for breeding. A good wing bay is a cardinal point in all forms of Black-red and related breeding.

Tri-coloured bantams provide some of the prettiest birds which are, at the same time, amongst the most exasperating to produce. Spangled Old English Game are, virtually, Partridge bred Black-reds with some white tippings to their feathers and should be bred as such. Others, like Millefleur Belgians and Speckled Sussex, have males with breast colour similar to the females and form a rather different group. Ground colour should be known, as demanded by the Standard and the shape of the black portion of the feather and the white tip should also be kept in mind. These points vary in different breeds.

Otherwise, all plumage consists of somewhat reddish plumage which has blue undercolour, a small area of black, surmounted by a clean, white spot.

Balance (as described for Mottleds) is important and should be the keynote of any breeding pen. It is more important that a bantam seems to have level markings than that they should be of a particular size or on every feather.

Additional hazards in this group are that the undercolour is strictly confined to the lower, fluffy, portion of each feather and that ground colour is clean and free from tickings of black. It is necessary, too, to ensure that the area of black is of reasonable size otherwise all ground colour is overlaid by the black area of the next feather and the general effect becomes that of a Mottled rather than a Tri-coloured.

Tails are always a bugbear and black and white portions must be confined to the tips of the feathers. All the main tail feathers should show good, clean ground colour.

Additional to all these requirements is the need to see that ground colour is level in hue and that all portions of the plumage match. It is worthwhile checking this point first and discarding those that have, for instance, washy breast colour before mating up the pen.

A difficult colouring which, when in good order, deserves full recognition.

Birchen (and Grey) with Brown-red bantams form a group which are compatible and are, again, somewhat derived from the basic Black-red. If depth of colour across the back is diluted and brown tinges on the breast are allowed to become fairly regular the Black-red cock can soon pass muster as a Brown-red.

This process of evolution has taken place many years ago and the Brown-red Modern Game, particularly, now consists of black plumage with lemon hackles and back. His breast feathers are each finely laced with the same colour as far down as the tops of the thighs. His hens are all black except for neck hackles and breast lacing.

Since they have dark legs and faces there is little difficulty in getting the black sound. In fact, solid black often brings with it dark caps in females and a heavy, dense top colour in males.

The ideal would be always to put really good show specimens together and expect them to breed the same. This would be a false expectation, some of the chicks coming too light and some too dark in colour. It is always necessary, therefore, to balance colour and quality of breast lacing in the male is a key point. Some of his hens can get by if they are not entirely laced round with a fine edge of lemon but the cock should have this point to greatest perfection. If the choice must be made between a male with too much or too little lacing, the latter should be preferred.

Unlike the Black-red, neck hackles in this colour should not be clear but are allowed to be striped with black in the lower feathers. Important to see that the striping consists of black and not rusty brown. What applies to the Brown-red is applicable to the Birchen where silvery white takes the place of lemon. Otherwise requirements are similar and the two colours are sometimes interbred. It takes some time for the brassiness which the lemon cross leaves to be worked out of the Birchen but the cross may be used if markings get so thoroughly out of hand that every breeding season is a disappointment.

Greys, as met with in Japanese bantams, need not be as strictly marked as Birchens. They can have striping in their top colour and breasts can be shafted with grey as well as laced. As in all this group self-blacks are sometimes produced and they can act as a valuable corrective to colour which has got too bright and gay. It is wise to use black females with correctly coloured males, rather than to put a black male with hens of varying shade.

Double-laced bantams, as Indian Game and Barnevelders, vary a little according to their respective Standards. 'Barneys' can be bred from one set of parents as their Standard allows some red in black parts in males. The Standard for Indian Game calls for rather darker males which should have sound, black breasts. To help this the females should not be double-laced right up under their throats but are solid black at that point.

Unfortunately, the Standard does not define how much red/brown there should be in the plumage of the male and they are now shown very dark in colour. Since the females are very well coloured and laced it must be assumed that these are, in effect, pullet breeding males and are acceptable.

Ground colour should be deep, even and thoroughly matched in all parts of the plumage. Undercolour should not be allowed to get out of hand otherwise each feather will have a short pattern of lacing. Small ticks and stipples, forming mossiness in the ground colour are not wanted. Lacings should be even, solid and carried well down the feather.

In general, this breed calls for individual mating and it is better to have a couple of pairs so that chicks can be marked than one pen from which parentage cannot be traced. When a pre-potent line is established it should be kept intact. It will then produce many showpen winners. To outcross will mean introduction of points which been carefully eliminated and much new work to do.

Jubilee Indian Game are also double-laced their white taking the place of the normal Indian's black. Problems are the same and they may be bred back to dark Indians in the same way that Piles are bred to Black-reds, when colour is wanted.

Chapter Fifteen

DOUBLE-MATING AND SPECIAL BREEDING PROBLEMS

Misconceptions about double-mating—its meaning and application—are frequent. It is necessary, therefore, to make a plain statement of the meaning of the term and how it may be advantageously applied to the production of exhibition bantams.

Double-mating has nothing to do with the physical union of the male and female bantams but refers to the selection of parent stock for outward and visible signs so that their produce excels in one sex only; the other being merely the vehicle for reproduction of the good-looking sex in the next generation.

In everyday terms it means mating a breeding pen so that winning cockerels *or* winning pullets are produced, thus putting the breeder a step in front of the man who tries to breed winners of both sexes from one set of parents.

In past days this method of selection—double-mating—was used in most breeds. Today it is only used when Standard requirements are such that winners of both sexes cannot be bred from one set of parents. It may be points of colour or formation of comb or lobe which determine that double-mating shall be used to produce exhibition stock of one sex only.

But, whatever the deciding factors are, they have no influence on the number of males or females produced from a given mating. Double-mating cannot influence the sex of the chick; only the appearance of the bantam produced by the method.

In some breeds—the most notable example being the Partridge Wyandotte—Standard requirements are such that it just is not possible to breed winners of both sexes from one pen. If showpen champions were mated together, their progeny would be worthless.

The reason is that breeders of other days set up as necessary points of virtue in the male and female which were not compatible and they have been perpetuated ever since. By selection for e.g. sound black breasts in males and well defined pencilling over the plumage in females, an unnatural Standard could not be fulfilled. It would have been quite natural for males to have some tinge of reddish-brown on their breasts or females to have feathers which did not carry fine pencilling on their cushions but these points were not acceptable. Insistence on black breasts and pencilled cushions resulted in two separate sub-breeds being developed to fulfil the requirements of the Standard of one nominal breed.

This position also arises in the Pencilled Hamburghs and one or two others, described later, in these notes.

Light breeds which have large, upright combs in males and falling combs in females should be double-mated for best results. In this case the male's comb, with a broad, substantial base and firm, upright carriage is naturally matched by females which have small, fairly upright combs which do not fall to one side of the face as required by the Standard. On the other hand, show females with their graceful headpieces are bred from males which have ultra-large, over-developed combs which are thin at the base and lean over to one side of the head. In practice many of them are dubbed for the breeding pen.

It follows, therefore, that showpen males will not have winning sisters and exhibition females will not have winning brothers. In both cases they would fail because of comb formation.

Double-mating is the obvious remedy; and is generally applied.

Any breed could be made into a double-mated one by concentrating on winners of one sex only and using breeding stock of the other sex, without regard to the Standards. It would be folly to do so in many breeds and would rob the exhibitor of his second winning chance.

Once the principle is understood, the problem arises as to how to choose the breeding sex which cannot be shown. There are no written Standards for such bantams and they must be taken on trust because of their parentage.

The greatest help in forming double-mating programmes is the trapnest and careful record. In the case of a pullet breeding strain the females in the breeding pen must be actual show winners or those which have been specially saved for breeding but are good enough to win.

They must accord as closely as possible with Standard requirements and must be level in quality. There will be little progress if one superlative female has two others of inferior quality with her and their chicks are not individually known.

The prospective sire is only valuable because he is bred from such females and will, in his generation, breed females of similar appearance. Although he may show few of the points which are wanted they are latent within him. When he is mated to suitable, related females he will assist in reproducing something which looks like the dams.

His sons will, of course, look like him and will be valuable only as pullet-breeders.

The recorded chick or the trapnested egg will be of great value in helping to build up a double-mated strain. In the case of pullet breeders the chosen cockerel should derive from the best hen. If he, in his turn, breeds what is wanted then all the progeny left by that hen should be used for breeding to the exclusion of offspring from others. In this way the general level of excellence is likely to be raised.

With cockerel-breeders, the male must be fit to win a championship and his mates should be bred from such a male. When it is found that the best winning cockerels come from one hen, her daughters should be used in the following year's breeding pen as well as her sons. If the other hens have failed to leave a notable son their daughters (sisters to the rejected cockerels) should not be used for breeding, since the appearance of their brothers is what is latent in them, to bring out in the next generation of males.

Briefly stated, a breeding bantam of the sex opposite to that being shown in a double-mated strain cannot be assessed on appearance and must only be used because it is bred from the best of the winning sex. Experience will later enable a breeder to choose a likely breeder as against an unlikely one but this selection is based on observation and such physical points of conformation and health as apply to any bantam intended for breeding.

For instance, no-one ought to use a Leghorn cockerel with a falling comb which also has a fish-tailed spike in it. This would be just as unacceptable in a pullet breeder as in a show male and should be rejected for the simple reason that it would end in the production of bantams with a serious Standard fault.

Individual cases of breeds which must always be double-mated follow.

Yellow-legged Black breeds such as Leghorns and Wyandottes cannot be bred from one set of parents. If the attempt is made the result will be females with dusky legs and males with unsound undercolour. This method is favoured on the Continent where plumage and shape are set before leg colour and soundness but is not acceptable by English standards.

A sire for the cockerel breeding pen must accord with Standard requirements and must be sound in undercolour. He must not be light grey under the saddle or at the roots of the hackle or tail. His wings must be sound and he should not have red or brassiness in his neck hackle or on shoulders. Legs should be sound, rich yellow.

His mates will, as likely as not, lack that soft green sheen which the male must have and their legs and eyes may be dusky. Neither of these features should be black, however. The undercolour of the hens must, like that of the male, be really dense and sound. They may not show any foreign colouring. This is a general guide but individual strains vary and, as stated, no hard-and-fast rule can be given. They must be bred from a succession of exhibition quality males.

For pullet breeding the hens should approximate to showpen quality and should have the correct top colour, yellow legs and clear coloured eyes, with undercolour as sound as possible. Their mate will have very good leg colour and he will be sound in eye but his undercolour will, more likely than not, be very light. He is almost certain to be white in sickles and may have some red in hackle or on shoulders. Top colour should have a lacquered sheen. He must be bred from exhibition hens.

Those wishing to employ the same method for breeding super-quality Blues would be rewarded.

Partridge Wyandottes, Pekins and Dark Brahmas, as well as Silver-Pencilled Wyandottes must all be double-mated. The essential difference between them is that silvery-white takes the place of gold and red when selection is made in Dark Brahmas and S.P. Wyandottes as compared with the Partridge varieties. Markings are identical in all four.

The exhibition male should have clearly striped neck and saddle hackles, each feather edged with ground colour and the stripe contained all round as in Columbian varieties. The colour across his back should accord with his Standard and wing bays should be sound and whole, as in Black-red breeding.

In every case his breast must be rich, solid black and his thighs, underparts and tail should also be black. There must be no grey in wings or light shafts to his flight feathers. Tails must be sound throughout, especially in sickle feathers and undercolour should be dark and sound. The sum total of these requirements would make him a winner in any company.

His mates should have definite and strong striping in their neck hackles, while bodies will be some smudgy sort of colour tending towards brown in the case of Partridges or grey for Silver-Pencilled, with very little pencilling. What there is will be coarse and ill defined. They may show some gold, red or silver on their backs and wings but this is not certain.

Undercolour of the hens must be sound but their otherwise yellow shanks and feet may be somewhat dusky. This is but an outline of the general trend and all points will not necessarily be evident in one strain.

For pullet breeding all the females will be of one level ground colour with breasts to match and every feather will be regularly pencilled. Thigh fluff will also show an amount of pencilling which will be carried to the top feathers of the tail. Eyes will be of right colour and legs and feet should be clear yellow.

The pullet-breeding cockerel will, probably, have no definite striping in his hackles, show indication of pencilling over his shoulders and wings, be dull in colour and have tinges of red or silver on his breast, according to breed. His fluff will be somewhat pencilled and undercolour will be less sound than in show males. His eyes and legs should be clear in colour.

Again, the warning is given that there is no Standard for the breeding sex in these breeds, but experience shows that the trend is as described.

A variation on Black-red colouring has been achieved in Brown Leghorns which must be double-mated for real success. Many studs today try to breed winners in both sexes from one pen and enjoy limited success. The top prizes go to the man who double-mates.

With minor differences to accord to his Standard, the exhibition Brown Leghorn male is on the lines of the Partridge Wyandotte cock and should be just as sound. His hens are of stippled Partridge colouring (see Black-reds, Chapter 14) but will lack softness in brown body colour and will have foxy sides. They also may show a reserve of colour by being extra dark in undercolour, rather ruddy on breast and with slightly dusky legs and eyes.

Show females should be used in the pullet breeding pen and they should be soft and sweet in colour with good breasts, shading to soft ash grey towards the thighs. Eyes and legs should be good. The cockerel to mate with them will have none of the brightness of the show male. His black parts will be tinged with red, his top colour dark and his undercolour light, with white showing in tail. His only merit is that he is bred from winning hens.

Pencilled Hamburghs are not of the pattern described as pencilled for Wyandottes. In the males there is, actually, no pencilling evident. The Gold-Pencilled show male is entirely a bright golden chestnut colour except his tail which is black, the sickle and covert feathers being edged with a narrow band of gold, similar to the body colour. Such a bird is wanted at the head of a cockerel breeding pen. Hens to go with him will be of a brownish-golden hue with some coarse pencilling on their bodies. They should have solid black tails unless their top pair of feathers are slightly edged, as required in the male.

Show females have pencilling which is, really, barring. Their ground colour is golden chestnut or bay, each feather being evenly barred across with black, as straight in the markings as possible. Hackles are golden bay.

Such should be used for breeding and their mate ought, properly, to be a hen-feathered male which shows pencillings (barrings) over much of his plumage but particularly across the shoulders and down the thighs, his breast also being pencilled to some extent.

It should be made clear that there are one or two true pullet breeding strains available today but cockerel breeders are just in process of revival and may not react as indicated. Pullets, however, will and no-one showing them also exhibits cockerels bred from them.

Silver-Pencilled are exactly as the Golds substituting silvery-white for golden-chestnut throughout. Pullet strains are even scarcer than the Golds and there are no cockerels for show, as far as is known.

Spangled Hamburghs are known in Silver colouring where the ground colour is white and each feather has a large, half-moon marking of black on it in females. The males are thus marked as to breast, underparts and tail but their hackles consist of white ground colour with sharp, dagger markings of black.

Present-day Silver-Spangled Hamburgh bantams are largely derived from large cock breeders; markings are somewhat crowded and not sufficiently rounded in females.

Because breeders try to produce both sexes of winners from one intermediate pen, many cockerels do not have the correct dagger markings either.

If anyone chose to get to the top in one sex only he would need to get the best possible cockerel, with good daggers and breast and a clean tail with large bold spangles, and mate him to hens bred from the same strain, but with heavier top colour and somewhat 'sharpened' markings to heighten this feature in cockerel offspring.

At the same time a pullet breeding strain could be created by choosing pullets with the best shaped markings and clean ground colour, giving an open pattern of markings which left them uncrowded, and mating them with a male with clean top colour but excelling in wing bars and steppings as well as bold spanglings on the breast.

The true pullet breeding cockerel probably does not exist in bantams but should be hen feathered and clearly marked on every feather in his body.

Gold-Spangled Hamburghs are in process of being re-made and are of the same style as the Silvers, substituting bright bay ground colour for silvery white.

Laced Wyandottes can best be produced by double-mating. The exhibition Gold male, to head a cockerel breeding pen, should be of show quality with clearly marked breast, thighs, wing bars and coverts. His top colour should be rich, golden bay and there should be a clear and solid black stripe down the centre of each feather in neck and saddle hackles. The back and shoulders should be rich, golden bay.

Hens to mate to him should be bred from a show cock and will probably be rather crowded on the back with heavy lacings but light on breast. They should have good ground colour and be sound in tail. Leg colour will probably be rather dusky or deep horn.

To breed pullets, each hen should have open pattern of lacing, especially on the back and cushion, each feather being regularly marked right round the edge. Undercolour should not be allowed to creep up the feather which would result in short lacings but be confined to the underfluff. Thighs should be as distinctly marked as possible. Eyes and legs should be of Standard colouring.

Their mate will have been bred from such winners and will have rather fine but sound lacing on the breast. He will fail by comparison with a winner in his top colour which will favour the ground colour of the pullets and lack sound striping of the exhibition male. He will not be as sound in undercolour but eyes and legs must be right.

Silver-laced will be similar, substituting silvery-white for golden bay and the difference in the males will be more marked still because any lack of striping or sandiness in top colour will show up more clearly.

Blue-laced are as Golds, with blue instead of black, throughout. Buff-laced are as Golds with white in place of black.

Special problems are encountered when breeding crested varieties. Polands, Houdans and similar breeds should have crests which, in the females, are of tennis ball shape and quality. In the males the crests are composed of long, shiny feathers such as are found in the neck hackle and should radiate evenly from a centre.

When choosing stock for the breeding pen all those with gutters or splits in their crests should be rejected. Even if smaller globes have to be taken, provided they are of good shape, they should be preferred to large, slack crests of uneven formation.

Size and quality of crest can best be assessed in the females and all of them should be evenly matched.

Taking a bantam in hand it should be examined at eye level to see if the top outline is reasonably domed. Holding the bird at arm's length and looking at the top of its head, assessment of circular outline can be made.

Looking at the front of the crest, it can be seen that it is firmly set on the head. With these points right, the bantam can be passed for the breeding pen.

Management calls for overlarge crests to be clipped so that the wearer does not become blinded to the approach of the cock and thus be relatively infertile. In order to keep the bantams comfortable and fit during the breeding season care should be taken that their crests are not wet. A piece of wire netting placed over an open drinking vessel will allow the bantams to get their beaks through to drink without getting their crests wet.

Breeds with feathered legs like Pekins, Belgians and Brahmas create a small problem in that they often become scaly-legged if not regularly seen to. The remedy should be applied as soon as the condition is detected.

Toe nails sometimes become overgrown because they are not readily to be seen on feathered-legged breeds and these can cause infertility. Remedy is obvious and examination should be regular.

Pekins, more than the other breeds, have masses of soft feather and an abundance of fluff. For easier mating this should be cut away above and below the vent of both males and females in the breeding pen. Mating will then be easier and more effective. It should be realised that such bantams cannot be shown until they have had a complete moult.

In those cases where a feathered-legged cock has great development of footings and moves badly he will be more fertile if feathers are reduced in length. When moulting time comes he should have some of the stumps loosened and removed, otherwise may find difficulty in casting them and regaining show form.

Chapter Sixteen

THE BREEDS DESCRIBED

Bantams can be classified in several different ways. One group consists of hard-feathered bantams, another of those regarded as ornamental and so classified by The Poultry Club, a third of light breed miniatures, the fourth of heavy breed miniatures and the last of true bantams which do not fall into any of the preceding categories.

Again, bantams can be divided between Game and Variety or between feathered-legged and clean-legged sorts. These divisions are not much help to the person wanting a concise description and opinion of merits of all the breeds. It is unsafe to generalise and attribute the same qualifications to every bantam breed included in any one group.

Instead of trying to group them, as has been done by almost every writer in the past, I have listed all the present known breeds in alphabetical order and given a summary of their extraction and classification, as well as a list of the standardised varieties.

After a brief description of the physical characteristics of each breed I have given my opinion of the character and potential of the bantams concerned. Here I must stress that this may be at variance with what ardent fanciers of the breed think. But I have this advantage—my opinion is unbiassed and honestly given. It is the result of conversations and correspondence with numerous breeders and club secretaries over the past 17 years and based on experience of bantam breeding in years before then. Where any particular details of breeding methods are needed they are mentioned. Otherwise it may be taken that the general notes on breeding contained in Chapters 14 and 15 will be adequate, if sensibly applied.

It should be stressed, at this point, that full details and the Standard points allotted for the various features of all breeds of bantams are to be found in *British Poultry Standards* which should be read in conjunction with this section of the present work, if best benefits are to be obtained from the information set out below.

ANCONA

Miniature of a Mediterranean light breed, soft-feathered.
Standard varieties: one only.

These are active, alert bantams which are rather flighty by nature. It is possible to have them steady in the showpen but they are always rather nervous and liable to be suddenly startled when on the run.

Most light breed miniatures have full, well developed breasts and backs of moderate length. Their shoulders are fairly well developed and long wings are held closely to the sides. Neck hackle and saddle hackle furnishings are plentiful and main sickle and tail coverts in the males are long and flowing.

Anconas are no exception to the rule. Legs are of medium length

A good pair of Anconas

and, although the bantams are apt to stretch up sometimes and belie the fact, the Standard says that their thighs are not much seen.

In the male the comb is single, medium in size and carried upright. It should be set firmly on the head, be free from side sprigs, thumb marks, fish-tailed spikes or other defects and the serrations should number five to seven. Each should be broad at the base and taper to a blunt point. Earlobes are white, almond shaped and smooth. They should be well set on the face, evenly matched and of reasonable substance.

Eyes are orange red with hazel pupil.

Legs and feet, with four toes on each foot, are yellow spotted with black and the beak is yellow shaded with black or horn.

In the female natural sexual differences occur in formation of plumage and the comb should fall gracefully to one side of the face without obscuring the sight of the eye.

The headpoints and face should be bright red. If the white of the lobe spreads into the face, causing the trouble known as 'white in face', this will mean that the exhibit will be downpointed at the hands of a judge. It should also mean rejection from the breeding pen for this indicates some weakness in constitution.

Plumage in all cases consists of black feathers, each bearing a pure white V-shaped tip. The tippings should be as evenly distributed over the body as possible and should certainly occur in the main tail feathers of both sexes.

The Standard allows most points for purity of white and tipping. It also asks for feathers to be black to the roots. This is not logical. No breed has feathers completely black to the roots. Even a black breed runs to dark grey at that point. In a breed marked with white, as the Ancona, it is asking the impossible and leaves the knowledgeable judge, who is opposing an award for an Ancona, with a very big stick with which to beat the specialist who is sponsoring a bantam of that breed.

From time to time rosecombed Ancona bantams appear in the showpen. If seriously bred together they could soon be a very appealing sub-variety. Their combs would need to be of the same pattern as the Wyandotte, q.v.

Anconas have long been noted for their laying powers. They lay a good number of white shelled eggs of good shape and texture which can put their owner into the awards list at bantam egg shows. The breed won the last recorded laying test for bantams.

As an exhibition bantam the Ancona can score well and has won best in show awards at some of the largest shows. There is a tendency for specialists to show pullets which are immature in head, lacking that grace which comes with a nicely developed comb.

This is a breed which is still fairly open. With sound foundation stock, many good wins could be registered. There would be plenty of eggs in the nest-box to offset the corn bill as well.

A specialist breed club looks after both the large breed and bantams and offers many trophies each year. It is The Ancona Club.

ANDALUSIAN

Miniature of a Mediterranean light breed, soft-feathered.

Standard varieties: one only.

From time to time a really good Blue Andalusian bantam is seen. Then the breed fades away until some other breeder re-makes it. Nobody seems to establish a strain and get it well spread throughout the bantam fancy. It may be that difficulties of production are too great for the average bantam breeder with his limited accommodation.

In type the Andalusian is much like a tall and slightly larger Ancona.

Getting towards what is wanted in an Andalusian

All the essential requirements of the Mediterranean miniature are there, as previously described. According to the Standard the comb of the female falls with a single fold to one side of the face and partly covers the eye. I am sure that this is a peculiar mistake which has been perpetuated by repetition. There seems no sense in it as a little more development of the same organ would result in a hen being blind on one side and therefore less fertile than a female which could see normally.

Colour of the ground of each feather is clear blue and this feature ranks for the highest number of points in the Standard—30. The lacing which surrounds each feather should be of medium width, black in colour. As this takes 20 points more it will be seen that half the total of 100 is taking up by colour and markings. This probably saves combs from being a central feature of the breeding pen selections and so many a hen can see which would not if it had a fully Standard comb. White in face and red in lobes are both bad faults. Legs and feet (four toes each foot) are dark slate or black and the male is almost wholly black in top colour.

My opinion is that this could be an interesting breed for the man
who prefers his breeding problems to be tough. When he got a good
one it should win well, but he would have a lot of wastage before he
got to his goal. Andalusians should lay a good, white egg. Many may
not do so because of the need to achieve colour by any means possible
and not only by selection, when strains are being re-created.

AUSTRALORP

Miniature of a British heavy breed, soft-feathered.
Standard varieties: one only.

This all-black breed is of today. It has been taken up by competent
breeders and developed until it is at a good state of perfection and wins
well in almost any company at any kind of show. Australorps have had
their share of successes at the largest shows, where they have won the
coveted award for best bird.

While graceful and alert in carriage their bodies are, at the same time,
substantial in build. Broad across the back there is a sweep from neck

*Australorps maintain
their popularity*

to tail which is all gentle curves. The body is rather longer than it is
deep. The breast is full and rounded and carried well forward. Wings
are compact and carried closely in, the ends being covered by saddle
hackles in the male. The tail is full and compact but sickles must not
be long and streaming although some still are. A point to be sought in
Australorps is a finely modelled skull with large prominent eyes which
stand out well and are placed high in the skull.

The comb is single, upright in the male and evenly serrated. That of the female is small and is best when remaining upright. All facial points are red, including the earlobes.

Legs are medium in length and spaced well apart, the hocks just not covered by body feathering. There are four toes on each foot; shanks and feet must be free from feathers or fluff.

In this miniature of a fowl, noted for utility properties, fine texture is emphasised in the bantams. In the female the pelvic bones must be pliable, free from hard gristle and fat.

All parts of the plumage in both sexes should be black with a lustrous green sheen and this shows up well in the best specimens. The beak is black, as are legs and feet which must have white soles. Eyes are black or with a dark brown iris, but black is preferred. The skin is white. Type must be distinctive and not confused with any other breed of similar general build.

Because of all the black which breeders strive for in their birds they tend to get it where it is not wanted. Some of the females are gipsy faced and some even have patches of black or purple on their combs. This is a bad fault which needs attention.

Australorps are still an open breed in which the careful breeder can do well. They will give a useful return in tinted eggs and surplus cockerels make a passable morsel on the dining table. A breed with a lot of virtues and not many bad faults—which does not need to be washed for exhibition, either.

The Australorp Club looks after both large fowl and bantams.

BARNEVELDER

Miniature of Dutch heavy breed, soft-feathered.
Standard varieties: Double-laced exist in bantams but others are described in the Standards for large fowl and could be made.

Barneys, to give them their colloquial name, have existed in various forms for more than 30 years. They have never caught on.

Lately there have been exhibited a number of birds which have, obviously, had an infusion of large breed blood. If the typical brown egg of the large breed has been introduced then the bantams may take on a new lease of life.

Barnevelder bantams should have rather compact bodies with a concave back outline. The breast is deep and full, wings short and carried high, tail full with a graceful sweep. Legs are of medium length, four toes on each foot, and the shanks must be free from feathers.

The skull is neat and the comb, single and upright in the male.

Earlobes are, for some obscure reason, described as long and narrow. The face is smooth as befits a miniature of a breed notable for the laying of large brown eggs and needing to be of good texture.

Eyes orange, facial points red, legs and feet yellow, are details which must be observed.

Colour is of general black-red pattern in which the breast of the male has been modified to red-brown ground with black lacing. The

Double-laced Barnevelder hen

back deep red with wide black lacing, neck and saddle hackles black with red markings, thighs, tail and underparts black.

The female has a similar breast to the male but all her body plumage consists of reddish-brown double-laced with black; that is, each feather has a black lacing around the edge then ground colour followed by another lacing and a centre of reddish-brown. The outer lacing is very broad and definite.

These, the double-laced Barnevelders, are the only ones commonly seen. If Partridges are produced they will have black breasts in males and stippled feathers with black edging in females.

My opinion is that Barnevelders will never make the top grade as exhibition bantams unless they also combine the potential for laying reasonable numbers of deep brown eggs which is expected from a breed of this name.

Specialist body, The British Barnevelder Club looks after both large fowl and bantams of this breed.

BELGIAN

True bantam of Belgian origin, soft-feathered.
Standard varieties: Millefleurs, Porcelaine, Quail, Blue Quail, Cuckoo, Black Mottled, Black, White, Laced-Blue, Lavender or Self-Blue, Lavender Mottled. Other colours are bred on the Continent and may be created here by intercrossing of the varieties.

There are two sorts of Belgian bantams. They are catered for by one breed club but are distinct.

Barbus d'Anvers

Have rosecombs and clean legs. They are small, proud bantams with extremely gay carriage. When on the run the cocks stand almost bolt upright and can be trained so to show themselves in the showpen. They have great development of neck hackle. The body is broad and short with arched breast carried well up. The back is very short, slopes downwards towards the tail which is carried upright. The main tail feathers are strong. Two main sickle feathers are not long and sweeping but sword shaped. Tail coverts are in tiers giving good tail 'filling'.

The neck is of moderate length, has full hackles and is convexly arched. Thighs are short and shanks of medium length. Toes, four and straight on each foot with nails of the same colour as the beak.

The head is of prime importance and makes or mars an exhibit especially in the showpen. It appears rather large. The comb is curved,

(*Left*) *Blue Barbus d'Anvers cock of good character.* (*Right*) *Mottled cock showing his full beard and whiskers*

broad in front and finishing with a spike or leader in the rear. It may be covered with small, tooth-like points or be hollowed and ridged. The leader should follow the line of the neck.

Eyes are large and prominent and as dark as possible having regard to the colour of main plumage. The face is covered with relatively long feathers standing away from the head, sloping backwards and forming whiskers which cover ears and earlobes. A beard, composed of feathers, and side mufflings form a complete ruff. Earlobes are small and wattles should be small or non-existent.

When viewed from the front, as this breed should always be when judged, the face should assume an owl-like appearance. This is more marked in the female than the male.

Hens are small and their neck hackles are thicker at the top than the bottom. They should appear very squat and plump in general character. This breed is attractive and charming. When a good one is bred it lasts well and, if good enough, wins year after year.

They are true ornamental bantams which are not expected to lay any quantity of eggs during autumn and winter. During the normal breeding season of spring and early summer they lay quite well, although eggs are small. Chicks are normally hardy once they are past the brooding stage. They probably do better under infra-red lamps than when with broody hens.

Barbus d'Anvers present a good opportunity to anyone who is content with the company and beauty of his bantams and does not look for a big return in eggs—although he may expect a fair share of prizes.

Barbus d'Uccles

Are single-combed and feathered-legged. Although they have basic requirements which are not unlike those of the d'Anvers it is usual to find this breed much taller and rather longer in the back. Longer legs are needed to carry the enormous development of footings which the best birds carry. The hocks have clusters of long stiff feathers which start from the lower, outer thigh, incline downwards and follow the line of the wings which are carried downwards. The front and outside of the shanks are also covered with feathers increasing in length until they form sweeping foot feather. Outer and middle toes are feathered.

In headpoints d'Uccles should not as closely resemble d'Anvers although, due to intercrossing for colour, they often do. The Standard demands a single comb which is fine, evenly serrated and of less than average size. The brow should be heavily covered with feathers becoming gradually longer towards the rear with a tendency to join behind the neck. The beard is composed of long feathers turned horizontally from the two sides of the beak and vertically under the beak downwards. It must be as full as possible and the group of three ovals of feather together form a point of great beauty. As with d'Anvers these bantams should always be taken in hand and viewed from the front when judging although the ruffed effect is not required.

Allowing for natural sexual differences the hens should follow suit. Age suits these matrons which are much thicker in body and more composed in the showpen than pullets, which always look a little slight in build.

Colours applying to all Belgian Bantams

Millefleurs, a complicated colour scheme which is of great charm but ought to be more simply set out than it is in the breed Standard. Basically this is a tri-colour in which the breast of the male is similar

Millefleur Barbus d'Uccles hen wtih typical feather formation in the neck hackle

to that of the female. A rich golden chamois colour is wanted for the main groundwork and there should be a black pea-shaped spot surmounted with a small white triangle on each feather. The tail feathers are black edged with chamois and having white tips. In the male the top colour is darker, toward mahogany, and neck hackles have black striping. The beard should be of black feathers with chamois and white evenly edged and tipped on them. In both sexes eyes are orange red with black pupils, beak, nails, legs and feet slate-blue and the soles of the feet must be white and not yellow.

In a nutshell, the ground colour must be right and the black and white markings as evenly distributed as possible. Although colours in Belgian bantams sound complicated the fact is that character comes first and it is more important to get it right than to concentrate on details of colour.

Porcelaine, are identical in pattern with Millefleurs except that the ground colour is light straw and black is replaced by pale blue. The white remains in the same places. Few bantams can equal, let alone exceed, a Porcelaine hen in full condition.

Quail, in the male, the effect should be of a little dandy with a nankeen waistcoat, wearing a dark cloak. With this in mind the colour scheme is beard golden buff or Nankin shading darker toward the eyes. Neck hackle brilliant black sharply laced and shafted with buff. Back and saddle hackles of similar style but darker. Tail black with lustre and faintly defined light shafts. Breast nankin, each feather finely laced with ochre with clear and distinct shafts. Thighs, as breast and the underparts greyish brown. Get the breast right with a good head and facial points and the exhibit is more than halfway to victory. The hen is on much the same lines but the chief points are clear and good breast colouring and a dark top which has umber coloured feathers with a silvery lustre. This is not black nor is it 'hard' in colour. It is not far from chocolate yet slightly different. It has to be seen on a top class specimen to be appreciated but, once seen, will again be readily recognised. There are very few Quail coloured hens today which have the proper shades of colour although many have the pattern right.

In both sexes eyes are dark brown, beak and nails horn coloured, legs and feet slate-grey.

Blue Quail are similar with blue replacing the black and dark parts of plumage.

Cuckoo have transverse bars of dark blue-grey on light grey ground. They are not, as so often described, black and white. Markings should be as even as possible, and each feather have at least three markings. Eyes orange-red, legs, feet, beak and nails white.

Black Mottled have lustrous black feathers as evenly tipped with white as possible in all parts of the plumage. Eyes dark red, beak and nails dark horn, legs and feet slate-blue or blackish.

Black. Self-coloured with bright lustre. Eyes, beak and nails black. Legs and feet, black in young bird becoming blue as they get older.

White, pure throughout. Eyes orange-red. Legs, feet, nails and beak white.

Laced-Blue, clear blue ground laced with black as in Andalusians. Eyes dark. Legs, feet, beak and nails from dark towards leaden-blue.

Lavender or Self-Blue, a clear, rather light blue which has under-colour of the same shade going well down each feather. No lacing or foreign colouring is permissible although, at this time, some of the males have brassy top colour. Eyes red with dark pupils; beak and nails horn; legs and feet leaden-blue.

Lavender Mottled as above but each feather to have a neat white tip, these to be as regularly disposed over the plumage as possible.

In my view these breeds have been neglected because they have not been understood. Once the basic character of the breeds is appreciated they may gain many adherents.

A lively and efficient breed club looks after them. It is The British Belgian Bantam Club.

BRAHMA

Miniature of Asiatic heavy breed, soft-feathered.
Standard varieties: Light and Dark.

Once reasonably popular and freely shown in both sexes of both varieties, only cock-breeding Dark Brahmas exist in modest numbers and good quality at the time of writing. Lights and Dark pullet-breeders are to be seen at Continental shows.

Active but sedate; upstanding but gentle; Brahma bantams are full of distinctive character and attractive in appearance.

The body should be broad and deep, square, full breasted and with a horizontal keel. It should look much deeper than it is long but some of this impression, to the eye, is from rather tall legs which are profusely feathered. Wings are medium in size and the tail is neither very short nor long. There should be abundant tail furnishings and the saddle, in the male, should sweep to the tail which is carried nearly upright.

The head is distinctive, being small and short with prominent brows. The beak is short and strong, eyes large and the comb is made up of three small single combs joined so that they become triple or 'pea', small and close fitting to the head. The rest of the facial points are in character and all are brilliant red.

The neck is long and well furnished, a depression at the back of the head being a further indication of breed character.

The legs are moderately long, strong and well feathered. Hocks are plentifully covered with broad, soft feathers and profuse shank feathering, also covering the outer and middle toes, forms the 'footings'. Plumage is profuse.

The female follows pattern, allowing for sexual differences of development.

A pair of Dark Brahmas demonstrate markings and leg feathers

In both sexes the beak is yellow or shaded with black and legs and feet are yellow or orange. Eyes should be orange-red.

Colour of plumage of the Dark is Silver-Pencilled and the Light is a Columbian, as described in earlier chapters. More points go for colour and markings than any other feature in the Breed Standard.

Comb other than pea formation and lack of leg feather are two very serious faults.

Anyone with a liking for old-time breeds and willing to show in classes for Any Other Variety until a revival takes place, can both enjoy himself and do the breed a good turn.

COCHIN OR PEKIN

A true bantam of Asiatic origin, soft-feathered.

Standard varieties: Black, Blue, Buff, Cuckoo, Mottled, Partridge, and White.

For years this breed was known as the Pekin. It would have been as well to leave the name alone, since is has very little direct resemblance to the large Cochin. Such superficial resemblance as there is caused the second breed name to be added to that of the club catering for these bantams, with a request to breeders to aim for large breed character. If ever anyone produces a large Cochin in miniature it will be very fortunate if it even gets in the cards in a classic show, let alone wins a class where every other exhibit is a Pekin, as known and improved over the years.

Carriage of the body should be forward and tilted so that the head is not much higher than the tail. The Pekin 'tilt' is a point of merit seen only in a few selected strains.

The body should be short and broad; wide and deep. The back is short and very wide. The saddle, in the male, should rise from between the shoulders and is fully furnished with long, soft feathers.

The breast is deep and full. Wings short and tightly tucked up, the ends covered with saddle plumage. The tail is very short and full, without stiff quills. There are abundant covert furnishings and the tail continues the duplex curve, going away with typical 'droop'.

The skull is fine and the beak rather short and stout. Eyes are large and bright. The comb is single, small and evenly serrated. It should be well set on the head. Too many male combs, especially in Whites, are rather large. A point to watch is that the earlobes are smooth and fine and almost as long as the wattles.

Great feature of the breed is the leg feather. Legs are short and set well apart. The thighs are hidden by a mass of fluff. The hocks are covered with soft feathers curling round the joints known as the 'hock filling'. Stiff feathers at this point, forming 'vulture hocks' are a fault.

Well developed but soft feathers spring from the shanks and the middle and outer toes. These should be so arranged that there are no gaps and the 'footings' are proportionate to body plumage.

Plumage should be very wide, long, and abundant. It should have a lot of soft fluff.

The female is of the same general pattern, her 'tilt' and ball cushion being even more pronounced than in the male.

The beak is yellow or shaded with horn in the dark coloured

Heavily feathered Black Pekin cock (left) and a shapely Mottled hen (right)

bantams. Legs and feet are yellow but a darker shank is permitted in blacks and blues, as long as the back of the shank and soles of the feet are yellow. Eyes are red, orange or yellow—the former preferred but not essential. All facial points are bright red.

The Black variety is single-mated so males are not as solid in undercolour as some other breeds. Lightish undercolour is allowable in adult males, provided it does not show through.

Blues should be clear, even pigeon-blue, free from lacing. The hackles of the males are darker in tone.

Buffs may be of any shade as long as they are sound and clear in colour with undercolour going well down to the skin. As a rule, a full golden buff is produced but a few females of softer hue have been seen and they have won.

The Cuckoo is evenly marked but not finely barred as in the Plymouth Rock. See Chapter 14, *Guide to Colour Breeding*, p. 80 for details.

Mottled Pekins are black with even distribution of white tippings. These should be of reasonable size and well distributed. Otherwise the Standard does not specify any particular shape for the markings.

In Partridge Pekins hackles of the male and ground colour of the female are somewhat rich in tone. Otherwise details are similar to those for Wyandottes and dealt with previously.

White Pekins are, too often, discoloured. They should be shining white.

It is practically impossible to write anything new about this breed which has been so favoured in the past and appears to be coming back again now.

The bantams are sedate and sweet natured. They easily become pets and can be induced to live in very small pens. They like personal attention and will 'talk' freely, when petted.

For these reasons it is easy to get them fat. When required to breed they will not do so. First, because they are fat and out of condition. Second, because they have so much fluff and mating is a difficult operation for such portly little bantams.

The best show stock are better kept for exhibition only. Others should be run together in a pen outdoors and kept rather on the lean side. Before being mated up the fluff surrounding the vent, both above and below, should be trimmed away in both sexes.

If footings are enormous in the male these can be trimmed down also.

While fertility may be 'dicey', no matter what is done, the resultant chicks will be well worth while and will win many prizes. Pekins are nearly always seriously considered before special prizes and best in show awards are made because the best of them are so perfect in their points.

Their breed club is the Cochin or Pekin Bantam Club.

CROAD LANGSHAN

Miniature of an Asiatic heavy breed, soft-feathered.

Standard varieties: Only the Black has been seen for many years.

The colour of the Croad Langshan is rich, sheeny black. Eyes, beak and shanks are all dark and there is no need for double-mating. Leg feather occurs on the shanks and the outer toes but is not profuse.

The short cut to producing something like a Croad Langshan bantam is by crossing Black Pekins with Old English Game. This was done by several people in the pre-1939 era and many small bantams of such parentage were quickly interbred; their progeny winning prizes.

Close examination revealed yellow foot pads; red eyes; incorrect tail carriage and lack of brilliant sheen.

Present-day Croads are on the right lines. They were re-made a few

A typical Croad Langshan hen

years ago and many of them now fairly attain their Standard.

Briefly requirements are a back of medium length but broad and flat across the shoulders. The saddle is well filled in the male and the tail carried rather high and well spread. The breast is broad and deep. Furnishings are full and there should be plentiful sidehangers in the tails of the males.

The comb is of medium size, single and carried upright in males; being quite small in females. All facial points are red and eyes dark.

Colour should be black with a rich, brilliant sheen. To gain this the darkest undercolour is not insisted on nor is a little white in foot feather deplored. It is, in fact, regarded as a sign of pure blood.

If bantams can be got to show pink between the scales of their legs this also will be a point of merit and cause them to be regarded as so much nearer to the large fowl.

There is often a class for the breed at the larger shows. At this time the Croad Langshan bantam is 'wide open' for development at the hands of breeders. There could be good opportunities here.

FAVEROLLE

Miniature of a French heavy breed, soft-feathered.

Standard varieties: Ermine, Salmon, and White.

This breed was first seriously put before the public about 18 years ago. The Salmon variety was exhibited at the Royal Dairy Show and was already in a good state of perfection. It has not made much further progress but Ermine and White Faverolles have been produced, as have Blacks and Blues.

This breed should be alert and active. The body is deep, thick and 'cloddy' as befits a miniature of a breed with table properties. The breast is broad, keelbone very deep. Wings are small and carried closely. The tail is fairly long, held rather upright and has broad feathers.

A strong head, broad, flat and short carries a single comb of medium size, with four to six serrations and carried upright. The face is muffled with full, wide, short and solid muffling. Earlobes and wattles are small, mostly concealed by the facial adornments.

Legs are short and stout, and sparsely feathered down the shanks to the outer toe. There are five toes on each foot, the fifth being quite distinct and turned up the leg.

The hen matches the cock, allowing for sexual differences but her back is longer in proportion and her tail is carried midway between upright and drooping.

The skin, legs and feet are white in this breed and eye colour is described (quite unusual) as grey or hazel. Comb and other headpoints visible outside the muffling are red.

The Salmon male has black beard and muff. His hackles are straw coloured and his back, shoulders and wing bows are bright cherry

Trio of Salmon Faverolles

mahogany. The remainder of plumage is black except the wing bay which is white when the wing is normally closed. Most males fail badly by being rusty where they should be cherry and having some striping in hackles which should be plain straw.

The females are very attractive with beard and muff creamy-white; breast, thighs and fluff all being cream. The remainder of the plumage should be wheaten brown the head and neck being striped with a darker shade of the same colour but free from black.

The Ermine is of Columbian pattern and the White should be quite pure, especially free from sandiness on top which is the prevailing fault.

Classes have been provided for the breed at the larger shows and have, at time of writing, been reasonably filled. Specialist club is The Faverolles Society which caters for both large breed and bantams.

FRIZZLE

True bantam of doubtful origin, soft-feathered.
Standard varieties: Self-colours and any 'natural' colour as seen in Old English Game, as well as Columbian.

Great Britain has always regarded the Frizzle bantam as a true breed, not even as a miniature of large Frizzles which were formerly bred. It has not been regarded here as a feather variant for Japanese bantams although this is accepted on the Continent.

Carriage of the male should be erect, active and strutting. The nearer it can get to Sebright style the better it is. The back is broad and short, the breast round and full and the wings long and drooping. The tail should be full and loose, carried high and the sickles should be full with plentiful side hangers.

The skull is fine, with short strong beak. A moderately sized single comb should be evenly serrated and firmly set on the head. Moderation is required in all other headpoints, which are red.

Legs are short rather than long and the shanks free from feathers. Toes are normally four on each foot.

Plumage should be firm, wide and well webbed but every feather should curl so that is stands off the body and points in the opposite-to-normal direction. The neck hackle of the male should be especially well developed to form a great mane and his wing and main tail feathers should also curl. Allowing for natural sexual differences the same applies to the hen where depth of curl can best be assessed on her cushion and wings.

In both sexes it is essential to have deeply curled breasts.

If curled feathered Frizzles are bred to other curlies, over the years the feather will become wispy and thin. The method is to retain a

*Small, shapely
Blue Frizzle female*

plain feathered pullet which is bred from curled stock and mate her to a curled male. Their offspring will then regain some of the width of feather and 'spring' which has been lost.

At this time Frizzles are badly supported. Breeders have themselves to blame because they have interbred colours until some of the bantams are of indeterminate colouring which cannot be properly judged and is not attractive.

The best bantams are now a few Whites and some of the Blues and Blue Duckwings. Those with true type stand out from a motley lot which have been indiscriminately crossed with anything likely to give heavy feather.

Legs and feet should be yellow in the lighter coloured varieties but are allowed to be dark in Blacks, Blues and other dark colours.

A really good Frizzle can win anywhere in any company. The rest are not worth the corn they eat. There is not now a Breed Club for this breed, but it is catered for by The Rare Breeds Society.

HAMBURGH

Miniature of an English light breed, soft-feathered.

Varieties: Gold-Pencilled, Silver-Pencilled, Gold-Spangled, Silver-Spangled.

In spite of the name it now bears the large breed, from which these bantams were derived, was English. Its history is involved and the make-up of present-day Hamburghs is complex. Such old-timers as Bolton Bays, Yorkshire Pheasants, Chittiprats and Dutch Everyday Layers all played their part in the evolution of Hamburghs.

Hamburgh bantams have existed in more less recognisable form since early days. It is only within the last 25 years that they have become really popular and this is largely owing to the efforts of a few Northern fanciers who started a club for the breed. This has now embraced what few large Hamburghs are left.

Bantams differ from the large ones in their non-acceptance of Blacks or Whites. These are thought to resemble Rosecombs to such an extent that it would lead to crossbreeding and confusion in the showpen.

There have been attempts, at different times, to create other varieties. Notably Gold-Spangleds with blue in place of black and Silver-Spangleds with the same colour variation. Neither have caught on and, as far as is known, they soon died out.

Most of the Hamburgh bantams are too big for the representation they are supposed to give. Large Pencilled Hamburgh hens are only about 3 lb in weight, although standardised at a pound more. Bantams will be more than half that and they seem to have arrived at the point where further reduction is impossible. They would be much more attractive if they could scale off a few more ounces and give the impression of being miniatures of a large breed instead of being (as I suspect) smaller versions originally selected from the large Pencilled Hamburghs and containing no bantam blood.

Spangleds are in better proportion although somewhat large for the very simple reason that breeders hatch their birds in the early part of the season to get full furnishings on their cockerels.

Silver-Spangleds have a good reputation as layers and are, almost, non-broody.

Graceful-looking bantams, these, with moderately long bodies which are fairly wide at the shoulders. The breast is well rounded and

(*Left*) *Silver-Spangled Hamburgh cockerel showing clear wing bars and dagger marking in hackle, with (right) a nice sort of Golden-Pencilled hen*

the wings large but neatly tucked up. The tail, in the male, is long and sweeping, carried well up, with broad sickles and any amount of coverts and side hangers.

The head is fine, the beak short and well curved. Eyes are bold and full and the comb should be fully double ('rose') of medium size, square fronted and firmly set on the head. It should be level and full of work but taper to a long leader with a fine end which continues the top line of the comb and does not droop or twist. Earlobes should be smooth, round and flat, of reasonable substance and white in colour.

Legs are of medium length, the thighs slender, shanks fine and round. There are four toes on each foot.

All Pencilled Hamburghs must be double-mated. The males are bred from one set of parents and the females from something quite distinct, if they are to achieve showpen honours. Spangleds can be bred from one pen but hens will be chosen to breed both heavily marked bantams (to breed the best males) and those with less black in their make-up (to breed exhibition pullets). The sire should be of good average merit.

Colours are, Gold-Pencilled male, bright red bay or golden-chestnut everywhere except the tail. This is black with a narrow edging of ground colour surrounding the sickle and covert feathers only.

The female has the same ground colour as the male with every feather evenly marked with rich, green-black transverse markings. The ground colour and black should be the same width all through. The neck hackle is the exception—this should be as free from black as possible.

In Silver-Pencilled, read 'silvery-white' instead of 'bright red bay'. The pattern is identical throughout the plumage.

Gold-Spangled male has rich bay or mahogany ground colour. All markings are rich, green-black. Hackles and back are striped with black down the centre of each feather. Dagger shaped tips to wing bows. Two large rows of bold, round black spangles make up each wing bar and secondaries are each tipped with a large, round spangle which form the steppings of the wing. Breast and underparts are marked with large, round spangles which increase in size as they descend from the throat. They should not overlap.

His mate is similar in general pattern but her back etc. are marked with round spangles and not striped or tipped.

Silver-Spangleds have clear, white ground colour instead of rich bay but are otherwise of similar pattern. Undercolour should, in their case, be as clear as possible and the main tail feathers free from staining. Dark underfluff is permissible but should be confined to the lower half of body feathers. Less would be better.

Markings take 60 points in the Breed Standard but, in practice, judges look for body type, furnishings and headpoints when judging and these must receive attention.

Breed club is the Hamburgh and Hamburgh Bantam Club and is in a thriving state.

HOUDAN

Miniature of a French light breed, soft-feathered.
Varieties: one only, black and white mottled.

Made, lost and re-made from time to time, the Houdan bantam never gains a solid following. The breed club which sponsored it in the immediate post-war era seems to have languished and died.

Briefly, it should be long and broad in the body, with a full tail. The head is large with a protuberance on top of the skull from which springs a full and compact crest. There is face muffling, large and full, almost hiding the face. Unlike most crested breeds the Houdan has a point of beauty in the comb which is leaf shaped. It is fairly small, both sides being equal in build and, rather vaguely, resembles a butter-fly.

Legs are short and stout and there is a fifth toe which joins the fourth back toe and turns up from it.

While the crest of the male has glossy, pointed feathers as in the neck hackle that of the hen is globular with feathers having rounded ends.

Plumage is black with white mottling as evenly distributed as possible. Legs and feet are white, earlobes white or tinged with pink, eyes red.

A somewhat peculiar Standard gives varying points for the features in each sex. I have never seen a Houdan bantam which was really appealing. No doubt many others have thought the same and that is why—except to a very limited number of enthusiasts—the breed has never attracted.

INDIAN AND JUBILEE INDIAN GAME

Miniatures of English heavy breeds, hard-feathered.
Varieties: one only for Indian and one for Jubilee Indian Game.

There was a time when these were thought to be separate breeds and were so regarded. There has been ample proof of them being inter-bred and one club now caters for both colours of both large and bantamised Indians.

In spite of their name they are truly British. If they had their due they would be called Cornish Game—the name by which they are known in America.

Attempts have been made to have Blue Indian Game accepted. They have been bred and shown but not admitted to standards. There are also what are known as White Indian Game in the large breed but these have not been offered in bantam form in this country.

Good Indian Game will win a lot of prizes and are never far out of the reckoning for best in show and similar awards, if somewhere near their Standard. It is the fashion to show them, males particularly, with stumpy tails which are less than Nature designed. Breeders would do well to select stock birds better and agree amongst themselves that fourteen tail feathers look better than eight or ten in the showpen.

Character is a great thing in this breed. Cocks should stand upright and look powerful and courageous. They should be active.

The body is thick and compact, very broad at the shoulders with prominent wing butts, and the back is short and flat. The breast is

Typical shape well in evidence in this pair of Indian Game

wide and well rounded and the body tapers to the tail. Wings are short and muscular and well rounded at the sides. Tail should be of medium length with a slight droop, sickles and coverts being short, close and hard.

The head is broad and the beak stout and well curved. The small pea comb should fit closely and eyes while being full and bold should be slightly overhung by beetling brows. The face is smooth and fine and the earlobes and wattles small.

The neck is of medium length with short hackle feathers. Legs and feet should be very strong and thick giving an impression of immense power. Each bantam should handle hard and solid with firm flesh.

Hens follow suit but their tails may be carried just a little higher and should be closely folded.

In colour the males are rich black except the base of the neck and saddle hackles, the wing bows and shoulders, the back, tail coverts and furnishings which should all be slightly broken or touched with bay or chestnut. In addition wing bays should show bay or chestnut when normally closed. In practice most Indian Game males are almost wholly black except for the wing bays—this is a bad fault which has developed in recent years and should be corrected.

Females are intricately and beautifully marked. Their ground colour is chestnut, nut-brown or mahogany. Whichever shade is obtained should be level throughout all parts of the plumage. Mahogany is usually preferred if a judge's decision is a close one.

The head, hackle and throat are glossy green-black. This require-ment for the throat should be particularly noted. Some all-round

Jubilee Indian Game are white where the normal variety is black

judges expect Indian Game hens to start their double-lacing at the throat but this is not correct.

All the remainder of the plumage should be clearly double-laced with glossy black markings which look as though embossed on the feather. There is an outer lacing of black, then a band of ground colour, another black lacing and a patch of ground colour contained within the second lacing. Allowance should be made for the belly, thighs and fluff to be less clearly marked than the breast, back and wings.

Legs, feet, skin and beak to be rich yellow or orange, with some horn shading on beak. Eyes pearl, pale yellow or pale red. All facial points bright red.

The Jubilee Indian Game is precisely the same as the normal or 'dark' Indian except that it is white where the Indian is black. White lacings are not usually as well defined as black and tend to make the ground colour look lighter than it is. When depth of colour is being lost in Jubilees it is usual to introduce a normal Indian bantam into the breeding pen and so intensify ground colour. The first cross may be rather heavily coloured and not sufficiently clear in markings but the next generation, bred from pure Jubilee and first-outcross, should be very near the mark for exhibition.

The breed club now looks after both Indian Game and Jubilee Indian Game, both large fowl and bantams. It is The Indian Game Club.

IXWORTH

Miniature of an English heavy breed, soft-feathered.
Varieties: one only, pure white.

The late Reginald Appleyard made a white-plumaged, white-skinned breed especially for table purposes and called it after the village in which he lived. When he decided to make a bantam version he did not stick to exactly the same formula for the simple reason that he wanted rapid bantamisation. Amongst others he used Jubilee Indian Game, White Wyandottes and White Rosecombs. The latter diminutive breed was wanted to give white legs and skin.

Ixworths have never become popular and have had but few classes to themselves. Not many of those shown have been accorded much showmanship because the originator always contended that the best birds could be chosen in the dark by handling for bodily properties,

White Ixworth bantams are a table breed

useful in a small table fowl. Consequence was that minor points of colour, eyes, heads and lobes were somewhat ignored.

Pea combed, somewhat on the lines of a longish backed, soft-feathered Indian Game bantam, all-white in colour, Ixworths are not now likely to make much progress. It is worthy of note that 40 points are allocated in their Standard for 'Table merits'.

JAPANESE

True bantams of Japanese origin, soft-feathered.

Varieties: Black, Blue, Cuckoo, Black-tailed White, Buff, Grey, Mottled and any natural colour as found in Old English Game.

Everybody, sooner or later, says that Japanese bantams are grotesque or quaint. Only their admirers and those judges who have bothered to study them see them as objects of beauty.

Japanese are not easy to breed, to understand or to judge. When their basic requirements and faults are known the breed falls into perspective and rather 'grows on' one. A prominent breeder of another ornamental variety has said, 'Nothing is better than a good Jap. There is absolutely nothing worse than a poor one!'.

This about sums it up. But there are too many poor ones today, both in type and colour. The main drawback to the breed is poor fertility owing to their extreme shortness of leg. When the point of desperation has been reached the breeder should try trimming out his bantams in the style that fighting game are cut out. With much of their fluff and some of their tail and wing development cut away, there can be great improvement in fertility. But the bantams so treated will not be showable until they have had a full moult and some of the cut feathers will need hand assistance to help them to drop.

Sometimes a Japanese bantam will come into the reckoning for high honours but, generally, they must be content with the competition afforded by their own classes. They are usually classified at the larger bantam shows and are most popular in the far West Country.

Character is a big feature and is made up of appearance and carriage. In the male the body is very small, low built and cobby with full breast and a big, upright, towering tail with large, sword-like sickles. The bird has a large comb which gives dwarfish character. It should have a waddling gait and be a mass of abundant feather.

The back is very short and broad and shaped like a deep, narrow U when seen from the side. The neck forms one side of the U and the tail the other, but this is better seen in females than males.

Saddle and hackle feathers should be long and full and the tail

*Good Black-tailed White Japanese have correct
tails and heads*

should rise above the head by one-third of its length. There should be a large amount of tail furnishing and the tail and comb may just touch, provided the tail is not carried forward in squirrel fashion. Wings are carried so low that they touch the ground under the end of the body.

The head is large and broad to support a well developed single comb, carried upright, and well serrated with four or five broad spikes. Wattles are large and pendent.

Legs are very short, thick and smooth and thighs are so short as not to be visible. There are four toes on each foot.

Allowing the hens their own natural differences they are cast in the same mould. In their case their wide and well feathered cushions show to better advantage than do the saddles of the males. The only colour which needs description is the Black-tailed White where all the body feathers are pure white. Wing primaries and secondaries are white on the outer and black on the inner web, showing white when closed. Main tail feathers are black or black with white lacing and sickles and side hangers black with white edging. The so-called Buff is a buff-bodied version of the above and not a pure coloured Buff. All other colours are as described in chapters on colour breeding.

Legs and beaks should be yellow although some dark shading is allowable in dark coloured birds. Eyes orange or red. Faces, earlobes, wattles and combs, bright red. The Japanese Bantam Club is active.

LEGHORN

Miniature of a light breed of Mediterranean origin, soft-feathered.

Varieties: Black, Blue, Brown and White are standardised. Cuckoo, Pile, Duckwing and others are exhibited and acceptable. If established, they should be submitted for Standards.

Leghorn bantams are not new. But they have only assumed a position amongst the most popular breeds of high quality in recent years.

They attract breeders because many of the old arts of the really skilful man, who can apply the principles of double-mating, are needed to produce a good specimen. They attract showmen because Leghorns will respond well to that extra bit of careful preparation in which they so delight.

They have their drawbacks and the main one is that they are, for all practical purposes, a one-season breed. There must always be an annual crop of good young stock for exhibition while the old birds, which have had a moult, are not much good for showing but can do well in the breeding pen.

In double-mated strains, such as Blacks and Browns where colouring varies according to sex (in the case of Blacks it is depth and sheen which form the stumbling-block to single pen mating) better fertility can usually be got and much damage saved if the pullet-breeding cockerels are dubbed.

Leghorn bantams have been selected for the honour of best bird in show on many occasions. Their wins have even extended to the

(Left) Well balanced Black Leghorn cock with (right) a White pullet which carries a well-cut comb in the proper manner

classic winter shows when all breeds are relatively fit and competition is keen.

Provided that breeders give attention to lobe substance, also texture and leg colour while reducing some of the lesser kept colours in body size, there seems little reason why they should not continue at 'the top of the tree' for some considerable time.

While being alert and sprightly the Leghorn male must not be stilty. His body is wedge-shaped, wide at the shoulders and narrowing to the tail. The back is long and slopes slightly to the tail which is moderately full and carried at an angle of 45° from the back. The breast should be full and wings, which are large, are carried close.

One of the main features is the head which should be fine with a stout beak. The comb may be single or rose but single-combed birds are almost always seen and a rosecomb is a rarity.

The male's single comb should be large, well set on the head, perfectly straight, free from thumb marks, hollows or execrescences. It should be deeply and evenly serrated with wedge shaped spikes, broad at the base. The comb should extend well beyond the back of the head and the blade should follow the line of the neck without touching it.

When rosecombed specimens are met, their combs should be level, firm and well covered on top with small spikes, the leader extending well back and not drooping to the line of the head.

The face should be smooth, wattles rather long and thin. Lobes are important and without a good pair, evenly matched, a bantam cannot succeed in the showpen nor is it desirable in the breeding pen.

Earlobes should be kidlike in texture, white or cream but the former is more fashionable and is preferred, well developed, open and free from folds and creases. There is no definition of shape of earlobes and this gives rise to argument. The preference is for those which are elongated oval in shape.

Legs are of moderate length with fine, round shanks. Toes are four in number, long, straight and well spread. Eyes are red and legs and feet yellow in all varieties.

The neck should be long, well covered with long, hackle feathers. Saddle hackles should match in quality and abundance and the firm body should be well clothed with tightly fitting plumage.

In the female the single comb should fall gracefully to one side of the face without obstructing the sight. In the rosecombed variety the well worked comb should sit firmly and squarely on the head, having a protruding leader. The tail of a Leghorn female should be whipped and carried slightly higher than that of the male.

Blacks, being yellow-legged, should be double-mated for showpen success. They must have the best undercolour that can be produced and beetle green sheen. Blues are self-coloured, without lacing.

In Brown males, the breast, tail and all underparts are black. The neck and saddle hackles are rich orange-red shading off to lemon towards the tips, every feather being striped with solid black which is confined to the middle of the feather and wholly contained by ground colour. The back, wing bow and shoulders are crimson-red or maroon. Wing coverts have green sheen. Primaries brown; secondary wing feathers deep bay on outer web and black on inner, showing bay when normally closed. The tail coverts may be edged with brown.

The female has a rich golden yellow neck hackle, broadly striped with black. The breast is salmon-red which shades to ash-grey at thighs. Body is a soft, rich brown finely pencilled with black and without light shafts to feathers. Tail is black, outer feathers pencilled with brown. Faults to guard against are ruddiness throughout and 'foxiness' on the sides. All the plumage should be of a 'soft' shade without any hard colouring or feather edges.

The White should be pure throughout but sappiness in maturing youngsters is a common enough fault.

Cuckoo, Pile and Duckwing Leghorns as well as occasional Buffs all follow traditional pattern in these colours. See previous chapters on colour problems.

The Leghorn Bantam Club caters for all colours.

MALAY

Miniature of a heavy breed of Asiatic origin. Hard-feathered.
Varieties: Black-reds, Whites, Spangleds, Piles, Duckwings or any recognised colour usually met with in Game.

One or two breeders in Cornwall and the West Country keep this breed alive. They show very good birds except that eye colour is not often according to Standard. Instead of their birds having pearl, daw or yellow eyes, many of them are red—which is a fault which keeps Malay bantams from high honours.

I like the breed. The very ugliness of it creates that character which admirers seek. Cocks should be gaunt and fierce. They should be tall, massive, muscular and powerful. They should stand high in front and droop towards the rear in three curves formed by their necks, backs and tails. Feather should be sparse. Their strong beaks and walnut combs add to their vicious expression and a light eye adds malice which is heightened by lowering beetle-brows.

Spangled Malay cockerel

Provided plumage is short and hard and character strongly in evidence, colour does not matter so much. A good Black-red follows the usual natural pattern and looks well. Spangleds are rather light in ground colour and also appeal. Whites seem a bit soft and feathery in comparison but Piles, although having much white in their plumage, come harder and fiercer again.

Hens never look quite so cruel nor so sparsely feathered. Those to match the Black-red cock are either Partridge, Cinnamon, or Wheaten; all being acceptable.

Commonest faults are goose wings in females and lack of true character due to the need for an outcross to maintain virility. In the largest shows Malays come into the money in classes for Other Varieties. Unless they still have the odd class to themselves in Cornwall they rarely get an opportunity to compete against their own kind.

MARANS

Miniature of a French heavy breed, soft-feathered.
Varieties: Dark Cuckoo, Silver Cuckoo, Golden Cuckoo.

When Marans bantams were first introduced they looked the part but did not lay the typical dark brown egg of the breed. This point has now been rectified and Marans can be strongly recommended to the man who wants a steady supply of sizeable, dark brown eggs; a passable table bantam and broodies par excellence.

Dark Cuckoo
Marans pullet

Many winning plates of eggs at bantam egg shows are now laid by Marans. When suitably crossed the progeny lay extremely good tinted eggs which can win in a different class. But the birds themselves do not fine down and their bulk is much against them in the eyes of those accustomed to bantams of smaller build.

Males are active and compact. They are well developed as to breast, front, thighs and body. Bodies are of medium length but broad and full in front. The tail is carried high.

Heads are refined, of medium size with large, prominent eyes. Medium single combs, well serrated, fine earlobes and wattles, with finely textured face, all indicate a breed with utility properties.

Legs of medium length and good quality bone, with four toes on each foot, are white in colour. Bold eyes are red or bright orange and all facial points red.

Females are of similar active but useful build, allowing for natural differences. They also should handle well and be of fine texture.

In the Dark Cuckoo, colouring should be as even as possible throughout, each feather having greyish ground colour with bands of blue-black regularly marked across.

The Golden Cuckoo has some golden barring and shading intermixed and the Silver is of lighter shade with much white in neck and upper breast.

It is worthy of note that Type is lumped with Merits to include type of breast and fleshing and quality of flesh in the Standard. Together they take 40 points.

Marans have probably come to stay as a useful breed on which beginners can learn their trade because their robustness will result in almost trouble-free breeding and rearing. My opinion is that they will never become an exhibition breed in the front rank for attractiveness and prizewinning. They do, however, enjoy classes to themselves at the principal shows.

Their Breed Club caters also for the large fowl. It is The Marans Club.

MINORCA

Miniature of Mediterranean light breed, soft-feathered.

Varieties: Black, White. Blues are more often seen than Whites and the time is overdue for them to be accepted to Standards.

Minorcas are much like Leghorns except that they have rather larger bodies, carried more horizontally. They should be fairly long in back and have well developed tails.

In both sexes the head is a point of great virtue. The male should have a comb which is perfectly upright, large and evenly serrated with broad, wedge shaped spikes. Five serrations are preferred.

Definition for lobes in the Standard still asks for them to be of medium size. High time for revision as, in practice, the bird with the largest lobes wins, all other points being equal.

Lobes are a 'must' for showpen success. They must be matched, smooth, free from folds and wrinkles and of good substance. There must be no suggestion of white or blue in face, no matter how well developed the lobes are.

The female should also have good lobes and her comb should fall gracefully to one side of the face without obscuring the sight.

Colour in Blacks is rich, sheeny black. Eyes are dark; legs and feet

Shapely pair of Black Minorcas showing good lobes

are black in young birds and dark slate in adults while the lobes are white and all other facial points blood red.

White Minorcas are pure white. Eyes are red, beak white, legs and feet pinkish white, lobes white and other facial points red. These are now so rare as to be almost non-existent.

Blues should be one level shade, free from lacing with dark eyes and leaden-blue legs and feet. Headpoints as for Blacks.

Minorcas have established two separate reputations. One as layers of good sized, white eggs which can win in classes provided for bantam eggs at shows.

The other as a good prizewinning breed which can take a turn at 'best in show' awards with the best of them. When a very choice pullet is benched really fit she will (and does) take such honours.

Like most 'lobe and comb' breeds this is, essentially, a breed which scores well in the first season only. A few, very rare, birds come out in the second year and win again. But the average show life of a Minorca is one season only.

There is a lot of room for the man who will bother to create a strain which breeds good showpen males with firm, upright combs. Too many have combs which are hollow sided and lobes which lack substance—both faults indicating that they have come from what is, in effect, a pullet-breeding strain. The Breed Club is The Minorca Club which caters for large and small Minorcas.

MODERN GAME

Miniature of a British heavy breed. Hard-feathered.
Varieties: Black-red, Birchen, Brown-red, Duckwing, Pile, Black, Blue, White. Various off-colours, such as Lemon-Blues are seen from time to time but only as isolated specimens.

Two mysteries need to be solved straight away. Modern Game bantams were made to represent the once-popular large show Game and are older than 'Old' English Game which were made at a later date. They represent a breed which has been classified as 'heavy' and must follow that classification although they are, in fact, one of the smallest bodied of present-day bantams.

These are only for the showman. They do not pretend to lay eggs, except to perpetuate their kind. They are next to useless as table birds and are not normally used as broodies. Modern Game are amongst the most delightful and beautiful 'toys' to be found in bantams.

When bred extremely fine in body for exhibition and the females kept back from laying there will be some trouble with them in the laying season. It has become usual to allow pullets to be rather larger in body than they used to be—but the Standard has not altered. Judges must still look, therefore, for the Modern Game winners amongst those birds which are short and fine in body with tall limbs and short, hard feather.

In a nutshell, the best exhibition bird will, probably, turn out to be a moderate breeder. It becomes obvious therefore that a double stud

A beautiful pair of Black-red Modern Game

should be run. One lot being kept for breeding and the other for showing.

A secondary drawback crops up when it is realised that double-mating gives the best results in almost all the colours but, notably, in Black-reds and Duckwings. Much is allowed nowadays by one male being put with hens which fall into two kinds—one having colour suitable for keeping density and depth of colour in male off-spring and the other having softer tones likely to breed winning pullets.

Modern Game need new breeders but the warning notes sounded above should be studied first. This is hardly a 'learner's' breed; the person likely to make a success of Moderns is the man who already knows how to manage and rear bantams and is prepared for some setbacks before he has created his own strain to give him a preponderance of exhibition bantams in the sex he most favours.

In management, Modern Game benefit from being in relatively small pens which enjoy some protection from early spring winds.

MODERN GAME

*(Right) A trim Birchen pullet
and (below) a stylish Duckwing
cockerel*

If allowed to run in exposed places Modern Game are liable to be blown off their feet during wind storms, with bad effect on fertility.

When good enough, Moderns will win well. Most judges like them but few can tolerate some of the rather short-legged, feathery bantams which are met with in some colours. Nor do they like to see something which has crept in recently—overdressing the thighs to 'clean them out' when they have, naturally, carried too much feather.

'Lift' or 'reach' as fanciers express it when a bantam stands on tiptoe stretching up to the top of the pen, springs largely from the thigh being longer than the shank and the amount of training which a bantam has been given. Get the proportions of thigh and shank right in the breeding pen and there will be little need for dressing out to make them look more reachy.

Carriage in these bantams is active and upstanding. Modern Game should always stand up to their full height when on show and respond immediately to the judging stick.

The body is short and fine with flat back, comparatively wide at the front and tapering to the tail like a flat-iron. The shoulders should be prominent and carried high but they do not always accord with this ideal. Wings should be strong and short and the tail short, fine and carried closely whipped. It should be carried slightly higher than the body line and the sickles of the male, which are narrow, are only slightly curved off the line of the tail.

The head should be long, 'snaky' and narrow between prominent eyes. The beak long, strong and gracefully curved. The comb is single and small as are earlobes and wattles. The face is smooth and, in the male, is made to look even smoother because the comb, earlobes and wattles are all closely trimmed off. This is known as 'dubbing', q.v.

The neck is long and slightly arched, covered with wiry feathers which are not profuse. Legs are long and well rounded. Thighs muscular and the shanks clean. Toes are four in number, long, fine and straight with the back toe well out and flat to the ground.

The female has, of course, her small comb, earlobes and wattles left on. Otherwise, allowing for natural sexual differences, she follows pattern. Key to breeding the principal colours can be had through Chapters 14 and 15 but the following particular points should be noted: Black-red male's hackles should be free from striping as also should those of Pile, Golden and Silver Duckwing males. In Brown-reds the neck hackles are striped down the centres with black of clean colour. Birchens are also marked in this manner.

In all the females their neck hackles are slightly striped with black except the Pile where the hackle is white tinged with gold.

In the Brown-red and Birchen the breast lacing must not extend lower than the top of the thighs.

Blacks and Whites are pure, self-colours. Blues should be clear, solid blue without lacing but with darker top colour in males. Others, such as Blue-reds follow the style of Old English Game in colouring.

Beak and leg colouring, as well as eye, vary: Black-reds have dark green beaks, willow legs. Eyes and all headpoints bright red. Piles; beak, legs and feet yellow. Eyes bright cherry red, facial points red. Brown-reds; beak, as black as possible, legs and feet black. Eyes, comb, face, earlobes, wattles are all preferred black. In practice they are usually dark mulberry colour but should not be red. The Birchen is the same as the Brown-red in these points. Duckwings have dark horn beaks, willow legs and feet, ruby red eyes and red facial points.

Whites are standardised with red eyes and yellow legs; Blacks with dark or red faces and black legs; Blues, red faces and eyes, blue-black legs.

Type and style take 30 points and it is obvious that a good coloured Modern Game bantam of poor shape should never win a class although colour is important and must follow definitions given.

A very active club, The Modern Game Bantam Club, looks after the interests of the breed.

OLD ENGLISH GAME

Miniature of British light breed, hard-feathered.
Varieties: chiefly Spangled, Black-red, Brown-red, Duckwing, Black, Blue, Brassy-backed Black and Blue, Furness, Blue-red and others derived from crossing of one or more varieties.

Although shown as a miniature of a large breed it is invidious to try to compare the clean lines and strength of sinew of the large fighting fowl with the prettiness of the bantams. Originating from Modern Game (originally merely 'Game'), Aseel and, possibly, some blood of the native bantams of the countryside, Old English Game bantams are now one of the popular breeds of the day and shows tend to base their classifications on them.

They tend, too, to appoint specialist judges whose knowledge outside the realm of O.E.G. is rather limited. Consequence is that when special prizes for champion birds are in dispute there is liable to be a one-sided argument in which the specialist will not discuss the other varieties—saying he does not know them—and the all-rounder is not allowed to criticise the game bantams because he is alleged not to know anything about them!

Old English Game are always smart and attractive.
Here are a pair of Blues

OLD ENGLISH GAME

Brown-red male (left)

Spangled female (right)

A very false mystique has grown around this breed as compared with some forty years ago when a bantam judge took all breeds with equal facility. This may, perhaps, account for some of the really badly coloured birds which are put up in the prize list against Old English Game of Standard colouring which are said not to handle so well.

None will deny the pretty appeal of O.E.G. bantams. Few, who have bothered to read and digest the Standard, could claim that they conform to the written word. One point alone will be enough to show what is meant. Description of tail is 'large, carried upwards and spread, quills and main feathers large and strong'. Fact is tails are compact, feathers carried whipped together, and outwards rather than upwards.

The breed is popular because it is relatively hardy, easy to breed because colour is largely disregarded except in Black-red (Wheaten) strains, easy to rear and prepare for show and does not cause the breeder any trouble to get headpoints right because they are all cut away from the males by dubbing and largely ignored in females.

All this means that the 'feel' of the body and the way the bird stands on its legs and feet have more to do with awards than anything else. Handling is 'all'—none, except fanatics, can deny it.

Carriage should be bold, sprightly and defiant. Any O.E. Game bantam must be active on its feet, agile and quick in movement. When these points are really good it is a pleasure to return a bantam quickly to the training pen and watch it become balanced in an instant, spreading its four toes evenly on the pen floor as it alights.

The body should be short with a flat back which is blessed with broad shoulders and tapers to the tail. The breast is broad, full and prominent with strong pectoral muscles. The breast bone is not deep or pointed ('keely'). The belly should be small and tight and the wings large and powerful.

The beak should be strong with the upper mandible shutting tightly over the lower and the head small. If there the comb, wattles and earlobes in males should be small and fine and red in colour. They are, for show purposes, cut away by dubbing. Eyes should be bold and fiery.

The legs should be strong, sinewy and close-scaled with a good angle at the hock. The thighs are short, round and muscular and these (like the tail) do not conform to the written description as much as they should. The toes should be long and well spread. Spurs ought to be well developed in adult males but fine and set low.

Handling, which is the beginning and end of a game bantam, should reveal a firm, hard but lightly fleshed bird. It should not be fat. When held in both hands there should be muscular resistance to pressure.

The female should be of similar make, allowing for natural sexual differences and is best shown out of lay. The Standard says the tail is inclined to fan-shape and carried well up. My observation is that to show them like that is to court the lower cards or none at all.

The great feature of this breed is its adaptability. It will thrive in a small pen with a tiny roosting shed or at large in a wood, where it can roost in the trees. Anyone can succeed with O.E. Game, provided they get the right parent stock and are intelligent stockmen. Few of them are ever washed for show. Most need little preparation and will score well as long as they are good enough, fit enough and well trained.

Look for no big egg returns nor small table fowls. They will brood and rear their own chicks but cover only a small number of eggs. They are not usually employed for this purpose.

Look, instead, for many classes at almost every show and a very big share in the awards for best exhibit. This would appear to contradict what I have already said but the fact is that these bantams are bred to a fashion and that is now very fashionable indeed. Nor will there be any change in the foreseeable future because the type and pattern of the bantams is set by the laws of genes and chromosomes while the Standard will not be altered because it represents an ideal.

The Standard colours are dealt with in notes under colour breeding, Chapter 14. Brassy-backs are self-coloured birds which probably have brassy-coloured (yellowish) feathers in hackles and certainly on the back.

Furnesses are similar except that they carry some colouring on wing bays. Their females are black or blue with greyish-brown streaks on breast and wings.

Polecats follow Furnesses in pattern but have some tan or ochre in their colouring. Creles have barring on top of some other colour e.g. Partridge with barring.

Salmon-breasted Blue females have salmon breasts and some salmon shafting on the wings, but are otherwise blue. Bloodwing Piles have deep ruddy colouring on their wings as well as the normal (Standard) breast and hackle colouring.

On top of the Standard colours and the main off-colours mentioned above there are now (unfortunately) a large number of bantams of bastard colouring winning prizes in the showpen, simply because they are of good shape and feather. Most of these ought, properly, to be rejects and are derived from 'off coloured' breeding pens.

A particularly unattractive bird recently seen was the result of a

Black cross Spangled mating: something which, in other days, would never have been done.

A very vigorous breed club, The Old English Game Bantam Club, sees to it that classes are well supported with specials at shows throughout the year.

ORPINGTON

Miniature of English heavy breed. Soft-feathered.

Varieties: Black, Blue, Buff, White. An occasional Cuckoo has been shown.

At one time it appeared that this should have been one of our most popular bantams. Of reasonable size and good breed character, with single combs and clean legs and as much feather as the most ardent showman would like to keep in order, they had many advantages.

After a strong start, when the Breed Club did a lot of work in sponsoring classes for them, Orpington bantams have gradually

Black Orpington female and White male are typical
of present-day winners

declined until competition springs from not more than half a dozen fanciers.

Others may keep them but do not put their birds on the showbench.

Orpington bantams should follow the large breed in style, having bodies which are deep, broad and cobby. The breast is broad and full and should be well rounded. The saddle of the male is wide and rising slightly to the tail, giving the back a short and concave outline. The tail should not droop and this, which was an original fault, has been largely corrected. Wings should be compact and carried nicely tucked up. This desirable trait still eludes most specimens in which wings are slightly long and drooping. The tail should be compact and carried high rather than low. The main feathers should be short and broad, sickles being well curved.

The head should be small and the comb, single and straight on the head, should also be small to match. Earlobes are small and elongated with wattles to match. The face is smooth and fine and eyes are full, round and bright.

The legs are short, strong and well set apart. They should be smooth and free from feathers but many bantams still show traces of stubs on shanks. Toes, four on each foot and well spread. Most of the legs (all the thighs and some of the shanks) are usually hidden by a mass of fluff.

Plumage should be profuse, broad and soft but fairly close and not loose and lanky. It should not be hard to the touch but of good texture.

The female follows the male in style, allowing for natural differences but her cushion is not usually as concave as the saddle of the male. It is in adult hens, particularly, that a tendency to drooping tail is most readily noticed.

In Blacks the beak, shanks and toes are black. Eyes black with dark brown iris. Toe nails, soles of feet and skin are white. Blues have blue beak etc. in place of black mentioned above and eyes are hazel or dark brown.

Buffs have white or horn beak, with white shanks, feet and toe nails which may carry a pinkish tinge. Eyes are orange or red.

Whites have beak and skin white; eyes red; shanks etc. as for Buffs.

All are self-colours except the Blue which has plumage of the pattern of the Andalusian i.e. each feather laced with a darker shade.

Smallest birds and best type are usually found in Blue females but there are few, if any, properly marked Blue cockerels.

High level of excellence is found in Blacks of both sexes, subject only to poor wing carriage in many males.

Whites vary greatly and are usually rather large and overfeathered, even for this breed. Buffs are large, rather too long in body and mostly of indifferent colouring.

Best of the Blacks and Blues are likely to win well against any breed in most shows. They have been awarded high specials on those occasions when seen in top quality and form.

The Orpington Bantam Club is active.

PLYMOUTH ROCK

Miniature of American heavy breed. Soft-feathered.

Varieties; Barred, Buff, Partridge; Black, White and an occasional attempt at some other colour is sometimes seen.

Plymouth Rock bantams are by no means new. They have existed in one form or another for a long time and many breeders of large Plymouth Rocks have tried to produce good strains.

The point has now been reached where the bantams are the mainstay of the breed club and generally receive a good entry at shows, both in summer and winter.

The Barreds are not notable as layers although they can sometimes 'turn up trumps' in this respect. Buffs have a much better reputation to uphold in the nest-box. Some Whites, where progressively bred from Plymouth Rocks without bringing in 'foreign' blood, are quite good, too. Any Blacks seen are usually sports from Barreds and no-one seems to have a true-breeding strain which can produce sound Black males. Partridges are a fairly recent amalgam of several breeds, in which the Partridge Wyandotte played a prominent part, and have still a long way to go to get proper colouring or type.

This is an all-round breed which should satisfy many. It is strong and easy to manage. It needs care in preparing for show but is not really difficult, provided common sense is used. Most of the females are fair layers. The surplus cockerels are big enough and meaty enough to be used as table birds. They produce their own broodies and can hatch and rear their own chicks. There are classes at many shows and Plymouth Rocks have won top honours, on occasion.

With nice upright, balanced carriage the males are smart with their deep, compact bodies, wide backs and moderate length. The breast, in a good specimen, is broad and well rounded. Wings are medium in size and well tucked up, the ends being covered by saddle hackles.

A medium-sized tail rises slightly and is inclined backwards. There should be good tail furnishings but no undue development of sickles.

The head is strong and carried well up, medium size. A short, stout beak; clear, bright eyes; a neat, firmly placed single comb; earlobes and wattles of fine texture, all glowing with healthy redness combine to give an alert appearance to the breed.

The legs should stand well apart, the thighs being large and all of medium length. Shanks must be free from suspicion of feathers and there are the normal four toes on each foot.

The female is similar, allowing for natural differences.

Barred and Self-colours are dealt with under their respective descriptions in Chapter 14.

*(Left) A Buff Plymouth Rock pullet with good type and level colour.
(Right) The Barred pullet in hand shows how regularly the best specimens
are marked*

Partridges need a little description because the ideal is to produce both sexes of winners from one breeding pen—something impossible with breeds of Partridge colouring which lay down different requirements.

Partridge Plymouth Rock males should be bright red in the head. Neck hackles should be rich, brilliant red with a solid stripe of greenish-black down the centre of each feather, but wholly contained by ground colour. The back and saddle hackles should match the neck. Wing bows brilliant red; bars, black; bays, reddish-bay. Tail black. Remainder of plumage rich, green-black slightly tinged with red. Undercolour, slate.

The female has deep, reddish-bay ground colour with typical, but strongly defined, triple pencilling on the main feathers. The fluff should be deep reddish-bay and as well marked as possible.

In all varieties the skin, legs and feet should be yellow and eyes are reddish-bay.

Prevalent faults of the day are slipped or split wings in Barreds; willow legs in Buffs; lack of type in Whites; dusky legs in Blacks; wrong ground colour and lack of green sheen in Partridges.

None of these are insurmountable obstacles to success and anyone possessing the right foundation stock should be able to be successful in the showpen in a relatively short time.

The Plymouth Rock Club looks after the interests of both large fowl and bantams of all colours.

POLAND

Miniature of a light breed of Continental origin. Soft-feathered.
Varieties: Chamois, Gold, Silver, White, White-crested Black, White-crested Blue. In recent years self Blacks and Blues have been shown.

I do not lightly subscribe to the view that these fowls necessarily originated in Poland nor that they are all of the same make-up. There are basic differences in that the White-crested varieties are bigger in build than the others and do not have muffled faces while the more compact Laced and Self varieties have muffs and beards which must be well developed. It is arguable whether Poland or Polish derives from the name of the country or from the fact that the bantams bear a 'poll' or crest of feathers.

A very old breed which, nominally, is a miniature of a large Poland fowl this bantam is, really, something which does not set out to follow the lines of the 'big 'uns' very strictly. The observer has only to look at the wings of a White bantam to see what is meant.

Carriage is erect and sprightly and the body is full, round and fairly long. A flat back tapers to the tail and the wings are large and

(Left) Silver-laced Poland male and (right) a White, show the great charm of crested breeds

carried closely. The tail is full and neatly spread but carried rather low and should have abundant furnishings. Sickles should be well developed.

The main points of beauty are found in the head which must be large with a decided protuberance on top from which grows a large, full crest of feathers. This must be circular on top and quite free from splits, partings, twists or gutters. It should fall evenly from a central point with feathers of the same character as hackle feathers, in the male. In the female the crest is made up of round ended feathers as found on the body and should not fall. It should remain in one compact globe and be as much like a tennis ball as possible.

The beak should have very large and prominent nostrils and eyes are large and full, not hidden by feathers. The comb is of horn type and as small as possible.

In White-crested varieties the face is smooth, earlobes are small, round and white and wattles are of fair size. In all others the earlobes and wattles should not be seen because of muffling.

In varieties other than White-crested there should be plenty of feathers to create muffs and beard which, together, should fit round the face in a full and compact manner.

Legs are fairly long and slender, shanks clean and smooth, four toes well spread on each foot. Beak is dark horn or blue; eyes, comb and face, red; legs and feet dark blue.

Chamois are alternatively known as Buff-laced. Golds and Silvers are of laced pattern and should be as evenly marked as possible. White-crested Blacks are all black except the crest which is pure white with a limited band of black at the bottom of the crest. W.C. Blues follow pattern, substituting blue for black, the former as clear in colour as possible. Selfs are of one, solid colour the Blues to be free from lacing but are usually rather dark in shade.

Some care is needed in breeding these birds which are often run with their crests clipped down so as to ensure better fertility. When being got ready for show they must be preserved in plumage or their crests will become worn at the front. Large feeding vessels should be used and the bantams should not have to push their heads through narrow apertures to gain access to food, grit etc.

Poland bantams, especially Whites, can hold their own against other breeds and have won many specials for best in show in the past. They are so well established that any good foundation stock may bring a new breeder right to the top within a very short time.

The Poland and Poland Bantam Club caters for them.

RHODE ISLAND RED

Miniature of American heavy breed. Soft-feathered.
Varieties: only one—Red. Single-combed bantams are usual but a rosecombed variety is permissible and sometimes seen.

This breed has aroused as much passion amongst supporters as any

Good shape and plumage in a pair of winning
Rhode Island Reds

other. They see all its virtues and admit few of its faults. Truth is
that it is a breed of considerable character and attracts because of its
breeding problems. No-one gets a monopoly so that others are
denied the main prizes. Consequently the top awards are well shared
out annually and interest is well maintained.

Were it not for the constant struggle to get and maintain a very
deep colour which is fashionable but not strictly in accord with the
Standard, few would have as much interest because of shape, feathering
or style.

This is a bantam of good, straightforward make and shape. It has
often been said that it is shaped like a building brick, with the corners
chipped off, stood on legs. This succinct description is pretty accurate
in the light of Standard requirements which demand a broad, long and
distinctly oblong body with a long, straight keel. The breast is broad
and full and the wings large and well folded, with horizontal flights.
The tail is of moderate size, carried well back and the sickles a little
longer than the main tail feathers. Too many still have streaming
sickles and long tails.

The feathering is close. Eyes should be large and prominent in a
medium-sized head and the comb should be of medium size, fine
texture, even serrations and firmly set on the head. Much room for
improvement in many cases but a welcome amount of attention recently
paid to this point.

The face is smooth, earlobes are well developed but fine and wattles of medium size. Legs of medium length and thighs large and well feathered with well rounded shanks and four toes on each foot are additional requirements. Beak, legs and feet are red-horn or yellow. Eyes are red and all facial points brilliant red.

The Standard for the breed goes into some detail as to points which are not wanted in colour of plumage. Suffice it to say that what is wanted is rich brilliant red with undercolour carried well down to the skin except in the tail which is green-black and the wings where the primaries have the lower web black and the upper red and the secondaries which have lower web red and the upper, black.

The female should match, allowing for natural sexual differences and she should, additionally, have black ticking on the tips of lower neck hackle feathers.

With colour taking 25 points and size another 25 there seems a clear case for choosing the smallest, best coloured bantam to win. In actual fact, the best coloured is often chosen but judges vary in requirements for type (15 points) and quality of plumage which is not mentioned in the Standard.

Commonest fault is thin, hard or wispy plumage in both sexes and since this is almost always of very deep (chocolate) colouring winners are often put up with these defects.

The breed will do well under almost any conditions. Winners come from all parts of the country and there is no monopoly. When good enough they do their share of winning in any sort of show and have taken prizes for best bird at the largest shows.

Many of these bantams are slow to mature and almost all of the season's hatch must be kept until they are fully up before the best can be chosen.

The best strains lay reasonably well and may be used as broodies to hatch and rear their own chicks.

The Rhode Island Red Club caters for both large and miniature fowls of this breed.

ROSECOMB

True bantam of British origin. Soft-feathered.
Varieties: Black, Blue, White.

The original native bantam was developed until it became the Rosecomb. Early bantams from the place of that name in Java must have been similar in appearance because the Rosecomb is shown at Continental shows as the Java and is found in all sorts of colours which we do not accept.

The beauty of Rosecombs is well demonstrated by this pair of Blacks

Here is another of the most beautiful 'toy' breeds that one can possibly desire. No good as layers, table birds or broodies, they cause so much pleasure when good ones are benched fit that they fully justify their existence. They are, in the world of bantams, what old masters are to 'pop' paintings in the world of art. They are, in one word, classic.

Carriage is that of a cobby little bird with one sweeping curve from the neck to the sickles of the male. The body is broad and short, the breast well up and forward. Wings are low, showing only the front half of the thighs. The stern is flat, broad and thick and there are plentiful hackles. The tail is carried well back with the main feathers broad and overlapping neatly. The sickles are long, circled with a bold sweep, broad in feather and encircling the main tail. There should be any amount of tail filling in side hangers which also are broad.

The head has that feature from which the breed takes its name—the Rosecomb—to perfection. Set on a short, broad head, a neat long comb with a square well filled front, plenty of small crowded spikes on top and a long, tapering leader. The whole should be set firmly and the leader should follow the top line of the comb, in one line.

Place also on each side of the face a smooth, round earlobe of nice substance and kidlike texture, white in colour. Add round, neat wattles, a bold expressive eye and cherry red face and the picture starts to build up.

Short legs, round, fine shanks and full beetle-green sheen over all parts of the black plumage and that 'tailored to measure' look is strongly in evidence.

The female should match except that she has her wings lifted up a bit and has not, obviously, as much development of head.

In the Black eyes are hazel or brown. Beak, legs and feet black. Blues are clear in colour without lacing. Whites are pure in colour with red eyes and white skin.

Rosecombs cannot be expected to breed and be as fertile as the larger, more robust sorts. They will usually be bred best in the latter part of spring and are better for some protection from the wind.

The very best specimens are double-mated. That is a male with large lobes and a very long comb but, possibly, not as sound in under-colour as he might be is produced by show hens and, in turn, re-produces pullets of that nature. They have sweeter expression and better formed leaders to their combs than cock-breeders. The latter are bred from a show cock and have very strong heads with thick, but lengthy leaders, which breed the sort of cockerels that are wanted.

It is possible to get some winners by using a good, average male and one of each sort of hens.

Rosecomb bantams are very much a one-season breed. Their lobes are such that the slightest contact with grit, soil or the great outdoors causes unsightly blisters which ruins them for show. They also tend to go white in face after reaching full maturity and few are brought out as adults. The best of them win well and can take any sort of prize at any class of show. They are worth all the trouble it takes to breed them because they are so very lovely and are living proof of what can be done to maintain perfection over a great number of years.

The Rosecomb Bantam Club looks after their affairs.

RUMPLESS

True bantam of British origin. Either hard- or soft-feathered.

Varieties: any natural colour as found in Old English Game.

This old breed is an oddity which continues to attract a few.

It is, in effect, an Old English Game bantam with no caudal ap-pendage. Bereft of the 'parson's nose' a Rumpless bantam cannot grow a feathered tail.

It is usual to judge the breed for small size, condition and brightness of plumage but many have very dark feathers and do not greatly appeal. In the showpen they are strangely mute.

Because there is no standard for Rumpless there is no reason why any sort of bantam which is naturally tailless should not be shown.

Blue Duckwing
Rumpless cockerel

Well marked
Scots Grey
female

As a matter of interest I have had a Black Leghorn born without a tail, thus qualifying as a Rumpless.

Since the breed occasionally gets classes at shows, it ought to have an approved standard which could be universally adopted.

SCOTS GREY

Miniature of Scottish light breed. Soft-feathered.
Varieties: one only, Cuckoo.

Just as the Rosecomb cannot pass as a Hamburgh bantam so it is open to considerable doubt whether this breed should be regarded as a miniature or purely as a bantam breed. It is said that it sprang from the same common stock as the Rosecomb, but was developed along different lines.

In general style it is much like an Old English Game, but with a single comb and red earlobes and wattles left on. Feather is soft and not hard in nature, profusely flowing. Colour is Cuckoo and should be clearly marked throughout each feather. Beak is white or streaked with black; legs and feet white or mottled with black but not dusky. Eyes are amber.

Colour and markings take 50 points of the 100 allowed in the Breed Standard and thus set the way in which awards should be made. There are few, if any, classes for the breed in England but it still hangs on in its native land. On the few occasions that Scots Grey bantams have been shown in classes for Other Varieties under me, they have done well. They always compare favourably with larger, newer breeds which are often found in such classes.

Definitely a breed for the collector of old-time favourites and the man who wants something just that bit different. If Cuckoo colouring is liked then Scots Greys are the answer to requirements.

SEBRIGHT

True bantam of English origin. Soft-feathered.
Varieties: Gold, Silver.

If ever the history of poultry breeding is written, the Sebright bantam will be very near the first paragraph of Chapter 1. These marvellous little bantams were man-made to the whim of a baronet and, in spite of their physical drawbacks, have persisted in strength from his day to this.

They still rank as one of the best of our exhibition breeds and muster a good entry at the more important shows. They still cause

their breeders to work hard to maintain their present state of perfection. It is hardly likely, after so many years, that Sebrights can be
made more perfect because there is nothing to which they can be
outcrossed without great loss of perfection in colour and markings.

Males are wholly hen-feathered. They have no male plumage and
this, it is thought, induces semi-sterility. The better a cock may be in

(*Left*) *Gold Sebright male and* (*right*) *Silver female show the perfection
of lacing attained in this breed*

his hen-tail the more infertile he is likely to prove. If males with curved
sickles could be used, they would probably have that added maleness
which would give them full fertility.

Breeders, therefore, try to compromise. They show short-tailed
cocks but use those which have just an inch or two of sickle development, in the breeding pen.

Each feather should be evenly and soundly laced with black, the
longer, almond-shaped feather being preferred. Common faults are
short, round feathers which crowd together on the back and breast
or those which, being long, bring with them longer bodies and lack
of type.

Many of this breed have won premier honours for best bird in
show and many more are likely to do so. When shown at their best
they are marvellous little bantams. They do not set out to be layers,
except to reproduce their kind during spring and summer, nor would
anyone pretend they had other useful properties.

But as morsels of diminutive charm and beauty they are as lovely
as anything yet created. Apart from the fact that all basic stock must
have sprung from one original source, Sebrights are highly inbred

because their very beauty is their undoing. When a breeder has a strain which is producing finely laced, graceful winners he tends to use closely related stock to maintain what he has.

It is only when infertility becomes unbearable or adult bantams suddenly die without apparent cause that he takes the over-late step of bringing in fresh stock. At the risk of being told by the specialists that they have 'tried everything' I would think that a system whereby several breeders constantly interchanged breeding stock would be beneficial to all.

Accept the fact that losses in eggs set and chicks reared may be quite high, what will remain will be bantams to delight the eye of breeders, showgoers and judges alike. Not for the first-year breeder whose experience is confined to bantams of $2\frac{1}{2}$ lb weight but for the man who has the will to succeed with something which is rather difficult—and very rewarding.

Carriage is strutting and tremulous, the bird often standing on tip-toe. Body is compact with prominent breast and the back very short. Wings are large and carried low. Tail square, well spread and carried high.

The beak is short and slightly curved. A rosecomb, square in front and set evenly on the head, has the top covered with fine points and terminates with a distinct spike which turns slightly upwards. Eyes are full and the face smooth.

Legs are short and set well apart. Shanks are slender and free from feathers. Toes, four on each foot, well spread. Plumage is short and tight.

In silvers the ground colour is pure white. Golds should be of one level shade of rich, golden bay throughout.

All lacings are even in width on all parts of the plumage.

Eyes are black or as dark as possible, legs and feet slate blue. All facial points are dark purple or dull red (mulberry colour) but males, particularly, are often red where they should be dark in face.

The Sebright Bantam Club sponsors the breed.

SUMATRA

Miniature of Asiatic light breed. Hard-feathered.
Varieties: one, Black.

There is, currently, a revival in this breed which, however, has not the benefit of an extensive following.

Pea-combed, very dark or gipsy faced, with sheeny all-black plumage, these bantams are of Game style with a very long, broad backs and any amount of tail furnishings in males. The tail should be long and drooping. Legs are black or dark olive and if more than one spur occurs in males this is a point of excellence. There are normally four toes on each foot and pads should be white, not yellow. Generally get placed in A.O.V. at the larger shows.

SUSSEX

Miniature of English heavy breed. Soft-feathered.
Varieties: Brown, Buff, Light, Red, Silver, Speckled and White.

Although Sussex bantams have existed, in one variety or another, for some considerable time they only gained a good following after the 1939 war. During war conditions many of them had proved their worth as layers and small table birds, being suitable for a back-garden pen. They fitted well into the 'Backs to the Land' campaign and were taken up by many.

When there was a move for better type but greater size in many bantam breeds which had not been very skilfully maintained during that war period, Light Sussex was a 'natural' for crossing with the large breed and then breeding down again.

In this way good character was gained but size went up. Markings became well established and few birds can boast such hackle development as Light Sussex bantams. This is not wholly good because it has caused keen competition as to which breeder could produce bantams with pure white bodies but large, well marked hackles which flow right round the neck and close at the front. The Standard has never demanded this; but fashion has.

Just at this moment there seems to be a slight swing away from this super-hackle form and winners at classic shows have been cleanly marked but with feathers of lesser size.

First in the field were Speckled Sussex bantams, then Lights and Buffs. The latter had a short run and soon faded. Others were developed at a later date.

Most of the Sussex tribe are good layers and all of them should make passable little table birds. Some may not because colour and markings have been made more important than minature table points. Nearly all Sussex will be good broodies and well able to hatch and rear their own chicks.

Lights win well at any show and often get a 'best in show' award. The best of them are charming bantams. Speckleds are constantly bedevilled by too much black in their plumage. None of the other colours are extensively bred and do not really make much progress.

(Top left and right) White and Speckled Sussex males with a typical Light female (below left) and a Light cockerel (below right) posed to show the definition of the hackle feathers and purity of body colour

Carriage, of the male, should be graceful and well balanced. There should be good length of back as well as breadth and depth. It should always be remembered that the large breed is essentially for table and the bantam is a miniature of it. Wings are carried close and the tail is of moderate size carried at an angle of about 45° from the line of the back.

The head is of medium size as are all the facial points except the eyes which should be full and bright. The comb is single, well set on the head and should be evenly serrated. All facial points are bright red.

The neck is of medium length and the Standard asks for 'fairly full hackles'—not the greatest possible development, as in many Lights.

Legs are rather short and stout, with clean shanks and four toes on each foot. Plumage is close and not unnecessarily fluffy.

The female follows pattern, allowing for natural differences.

The Brown ·is only seen at the largest shows and continues to be rather large. It is, in effect, a natural Black-red in colouring and should have red eyes. Buff is a Buff-Columbian, pattern of markings being as in the Light but with Buff body colour and clear undercolour, if possible. Eyes red.

The Light is the most popular variety and breeding methods are dealt with in chapter on colour breeding. Red Sussex are small, neat and attractive but completely overshadowed by Rhode Island Reds which they resemble somewhat. Main differences are hackle striping and slate undercolour in the Sussex, as well as basic type. Eyes orange.

Silvers are a variety on their own. In the male the head, neck and saddle hackles are silvery white striped as in the Light. Back and wing bow are silvery white. Wing bar is black. Flights and secondaries are black with grey markings. Breast black with silver lacing and white shafts to feathers. Thighs dark grey faintly laced with silver. Tail black and undercolour grey.

Female has head and hackle as described for male. Back and wing bow grey-black, with white shaft and fine silver edgings to feathers. Flights and secondaries grey-black. Tail black. Breast and thighs a lighter shade of grey-black with white shafts and silver lacing. A common fault is willow shading in shanks. Eyes orange.

Speckled is a tri-coloured variety which should have dark mahogany ground colour and with the breast of the male equating to that of the female. Frequently of excellent type but rather coarsely made. Eyes red.

Whites should be one colour throughout and are often of variable type. Eyes orange.

Sussex are strong and hardy bantams. They will breed and rear well and there are classes at all the larger shows with the odd class at small shows, as well.

On several occasions, eggs which have scored well in classes for 'contents' have been described to me as being laid by Sussex bantams. It says much for their abilities that these good eggs have been encountered at all seasons of the year.

The Sussex Poultry Club of Great Britain looks after both large and bantams.

WELSUMMER

Miniature of a Dutch light breed. Soft-feathered.

Varieties: only one seen in bantams although there is also a Silver Duckwing in large fowl which would have to be accepted to standards, if made.

Everything about the Welsummer is 'natural'. Conformation is such that there are no exaggerations of any kind. Comb is simple, single type. There are no adornments on the legs or feet. Colour is natural black-red which has not been developed to such a point that double-mating is needed. Winners of both sexes are bred from the same pen.

Although Welsummers are classified as a light breed, they lay deep

Typical Welsummer pullet, a winner which could lay deep brown eggs

brown, matt-surfaced eggs. Bantams follow suit and their products can win prizes in bantam egg classes.

In its earliest days the Welsummer bantam suffered because birds containing some Black-red Old English Game blood could easily be made to pass in general appearance. They did not lay the typical brown egg. Modern strains have got over this drawback and Welsummers are now bantams which should suit the man who likes something easy to manage, easy to show and easy to reproduce.

There are classes at some of the larger shows which are, usually, taken by a specialist club judge.

Carriage is very active and upright, the bantam being alert. Body should have good length and width, the tail being carried high to betoken vitality. The head should be refined. The comb, in the male, is firmly set on the head and well serrated. Eyes should be bold and feet and legs straight and strong. Four toes on each foot and shanks quite free from fluff or feather. Texture should be apparent in skin and plumage.

Colour is natural black-red, the male's hackles being free from striping. Some red mottling is permissible on breast and fluff. In the female the rich chestnut red of the breast and the reddish-brown colouring of the back, coupled with small stippling of black, also allow brothers and sisters from the one pen to be winners in the showpen.

Beak, yellow or horn. Legs and feet yellow, undercolour dark slate grey. All facial points and eyes are red.

The Welsummer Club looks after both large and bantams.

WYANDOTTE

Miniature of American heavy breed. Soft-feathered.

Varieties: Black, Blue, Buff, Columbian, Gold-Laced, Mottled, Partridge, Silver-Laced, Silver-Pencilled, White. Also seen, from time to time, are Violette (Blue-Laced), Buff Columbian, Buff-Laced (White-Laced Buffs), Crele and Cuckoo.

With the possible exception of Belgian bantams no soft-feathered breed has been produced in as many varieties as the Wyandotte. Most of them are passably good and attractive. All of them could be fascinating if their breeders bothered to raise enough to make their experiments worth while. Too often they breed few and show less. When the variety attracts a newcomer there is no good foundation stock to spare for him.

Because of their shape and general mould, allied to serene expression and good deportment, all Wyandottes attract. Few can resist their charms even if they do not actually breed Wyandottes.

They have won high awards at all sorts of shows on many occasions, chiefly through their White, Black and Partridge representatives, although Laced have scored quite well recently.

It is usual to describe the Wyandotte as a bird of curves. I cannot

Although White Wyandottes are the most popular, other attractive members of the family are the Partridge and Columbian (top left and right) as well as the Black and Silver-Laced (below)

quarrel with that description. There should not be a flat line anywhere on the body. All parts must subscribe to the general requirement of gentle curves in all directions.

They are well balanced and graceful, alert in manner but docile in temperament. The body is short and deep, well rounded at the sides. The back is short with a full, broad saddle in the male which sweeps to the tail with a concave rise. The breast is round and full.

Wings are of medium size, folded closely to the body, the tail being full and short. It is, however, well developed and should be fully furnished.

The head is broad and short with a stout beak. The comb is broad at the front, fully double ('rose') tapering to a leader or spike at the back and this is carried downwards, following the line of the neck. The whole should fit nicely over the head and be covered over the top with many small spikes or 'work'.

The face is smooth and fine, the earlobes oblong and the wattles are well rounded.

The neck is arched with a full hackle and plumage is close and silky with abundant fluff which should not be long.

Legs are of medium length, shanks strong and feet well spread, four toes on each foot.

The hen should follow pattern and her cushion should not be so full that it droops at the tail ('ball cushioned') nor yet scant so that her rear is out of balance with her front.

Beak yellow or shaded with horn in the dark varieties. Legs and feet yellow, eyes bright bay (not red, as commonly said). All facial points red.

Notes on breeding all the colours are given in Chapters 14 and 15. Blacks, being yellow-legged, must be double-mated for success. Blues should be even and medium shade, without lacing. Buffs are self-coloured and should be even. Columbian are marked as in Light Brahmas and Sussex.

Gold-Laced and Silver-Laced, as well as Blue-Laced and White-Laced Buff, all conform to one pattern, ground colour and markings varying in shade. The Mottled are as in Pekins. Partridge are, virtually, two distinct breeds under one varietal name and are fully described in previous chapters. Silver-Pencilled follow suit, except for ground colour which is silvery-white. Cuckoos are barred, with an open pattern of marking.

It would be wrong to claim that Wyandottes are amongst today's best laying bantams, although they were when I first bred them, some forty years ago. They have now been bred for shows for so long that they have become very perfect and will win a handful of prizes almost everywhere.

Mating, breeding and rearing do not present any very great difficulties and the breed is docile and quite easy to train for showing.

They will succeed anywhere within reason and do very well in small spaces. No reason to suppose that they will lose popularity in the near future; new breeders are always coming along.

Several of the different Clubs cater for both large and bantams e.g. The Laced Wyandotte Club, but the one body which looks after all the colours is The Wyandotte Bantam Club.

YOKOHAMA

Miniature of Asiatic light breed, soft-feathered.

Varieties: any natural Game colour is acceptable.

There is always somebody, somewhere, working on a revival of this breed which is notable for great length of tail development.

On the lines of a rather long-backed Old English Game, the Yokohama is not as small in body and must carry a tail at least twice

Duckwing Yokohama cockerel showing low tail carriage and some of the development required

the length of the body, if it is to be anywhere near the target. Hens should also have long tails and should carry them low and 'play' them loosely not holding them whipped or rigid in manner.

When these bantams are single-combed they are Yokohamas but if a pea-combed variety is produced it should be known as the Phoenix.

Facial colour, eyes, legs and feet, should follow the natural colouring for O.E. Game. Examples, a Brown-red would be dark in face, eyes and legs. A Duckwing would be red-eyed, and either white, yellow or willow in legs and feet.

OTHER BREEDS

Araucanas, should always be pea-combed but some bantams shown under this name are crested. Another feature is that females lay blue-shelled eggs.

Aseels, very little known or bred. Only shown once to my recollection. Hard-feathered, like a small, original type Indian Game of reddish (Black-red) colouring.

Booted, in effect a clean faced Barbus d'Uccles which has now been put out of favour by that breed.

Dorkings, usually someone re-makes them in Silver-grey colouring and keeps them for a few seasons but they always languish from lack of interest. Five toes on each foot are essential.

Nankins, small, sprightly, natural bantams. Ochre (original buff-type) colouring and blue legs do not attract the modern eye.

Redcaps, miniatures of a breed once well known in the West Riding of Yorkshire and the Derbyshire Peak District as a good layer. Chiefly notable for the extra large 'cap' comb but never really popular. Last produced by a fancier in Nottinghamshire but not now existing, as far as is known.

Scots Dumpies, very short in the leg and otherwise like a 'dumpy' Scots Grey. I have not seen a specimen for something like 15 years. Very infertile due to short shanks and inbreeding.

Chapter Seventeen

BANTAMS AS LAYERS

Many claims are made by enthusiasts as to the laying abilities of their bantams. Many of these, unfortunately, cannot be substantiated.

It is as well, therefore, to remember that nearly all bantams are primarily bred for exhibition and surplus pullets from them have not been bred with laying as their prime purpose in life.

Under certain conditions and in small units, they may lay quite well. But if a supply of new laid eggs is the sole object of poultry keeping then bantams would not be first choice.

There have been one or two laying tests for bantams and their records tend to prove what is stated above. The last such test ended in autumn 1952 after bantams had been kept under Battery conditions for 48 weeks.

72 bantams laid 7,643 eggs during the 48 weeks' period, giving a 'hen housed' average of 106 eggs per bird and a 'standard' average of 108·41. Mortality totalled 8·33%.

The average daily consumption of food was 3·57 oz per bird.

For purposes of comparison it can be stated that records prove 824 large breed pullets averaged 184·5 eggs (standard) with a mortality of 11·80%. Their average daily consumption of food was approximately 6 oz per bird.

This particular test for bantams was won by Anconas with the average of 161 eggs per bird, their best performer laying 189 eggs. The three bantams in this pen laid 483 eggs for a food consumption of 242 lb, with a feed conversion rate of 5·46 lb of food for each 1 lb of eggs.

If the body weight of the bantams had been recorded it would

*Nicely matched plate of eggs
as they should be exhibited at
a show*

have been helpful as there was a distinct impression, at the time, that these bantams were oversized as compared with exhibition birds. All the same they were bantams and bred from them.

The next best performance at the laying test in 1952 was put up by Rhode Island Reds whose average was 157·6 eggs per bird. They laid 473 eggs for 231 lb of food and had a feed conversion rate of 5·24 lb for each 1 lb of eggs.

An analysis, published at the time, showed that 29% of all eggs laid were bantam super ($1\frac{1}{2}$-$1\frac{3}{4}$ oz) and 58% were standard ($1\frac{1}{4}$-$1\frac{1}{2}$ oz).

Since those days there has been a big move towards exhibiting bantam eggs in classes provided especially for them at the shows. One one occasion it was my duty to doubt whether some of the eggs which scaled near 2 oz were the product of true bantams or whether they came from near-large-breed pullets with some bantam blood in them. There are now several breeds which will lay eggs equal to the super grade described above. Their products are of good shape and texture, uniform in colour and capable of being well matched to form a winning plate.

In classes for brown eggs those laid by Marans often win, having rich colouring and nice shape. Welsummers also lay an egg typical of that expected from the breed, wonderful shape and texture but rather matt coffee brown which does not always stand up to close competition from the darker Marans products.

In the tinted section Sussex generally score well and there have been occasions when Sussex bantam eggs have done well in classes for contents, competing with all large and bantam breeds.

Rhode Island Reds of some strains, Buff Plymouth Rocks, Australorps and some Wyandottes also lay good tinted eggs. Of these Australorps are, perhaps, the most consistent.

White-shelled eggs which win are likely to be laid by Black Minorcas but Anconas, some Leghorns and Hamburghs also do well.

The Poultry Club standard for eggs intended for exhibition demands that they are of right shape, showing ample breadth with a good dome, and greater length than width.

Size, for bantams, should be as indicated above and should be accounted for by quality of contents, not bulk. Shell texture shall be closely knit free from pimples, bulges and roughness.

Shells shall be cleaned but not otherwise prepared in any way, the air-space at the dome end being small to indicate freshness. When three or six eggs are shown in one plate they shall be well matched and uniform in appearance, all being fresh.

Points are awarded for shape, size, shell texture, colour, freshness including bloom and appearance, each feature meriting 20 points.

Some bantams will lay a reasonable amount of eggs, but they may not perform very well during the worst of winter weather nor during late summer. Since they have not been selected for laying they cannot be expected to give the same performance as bred-to-lay fowls. They will, however, pay for much of their keep if properly managed and are housed suitably for winter laying.

Chapter Eighteen

AN ABC OF COMMON TERMS
AND AILMENTS

ABNORMAL EGGS Likely from young pullets, just coming into lay, which have not adjusted themselves to the rhythm of production. Frequently become normal as laying proceeds. Persistent layers of abnormal eggs should be excluded from the breeding pen as the factor can be inherited. Causes which can be remedied include excess of internal fat, too forcing a diet and fright or shock.

ABSCESS An accumulation of pus at a point of the body. Apart from those which follow injury, most likely to be found if bantams have bumble foot.

ADDLED EGG An egg which has been partially incubated and in which the embryo has died at an early period. Hence, a fertile egg containing a dead embryo.

AGE OF BREEDING STOCK No hard-and-fast rule on this point. Many breeders of ornamental bantams stick to proven breeding stock, in pairs, regardless of age. Keynote is strength and vigour on both sides of the pen, age being counterbalanced with youth.

ALBUMEN When eggs are broken (as at shows, in 'contents' classes) the albumen must be thick and firm and not watery. This will follow good feeding or the use of an extensive stray.

AMMONIA. After an outbreak of coccidiosis, a 10% household ammonia is helpful in cleaning both houses and brooding equipment.

ANAEMIA Deficiency of blood, showing as pale headpoints and listlessness. May be caused by worms, red mite or unbalanced feeding. Individual cases can be helped by penning separately and giving an iron tonic, as well as easily digested, nourishing food.

ANIMAL PROTEIN   Foods derived from animal sources such as fish or meat meal. 5% added to the ordinary mash will help feather growth at moulting time.

ANTIBIOTICS   Substances produced by a living mould which are used to combat certain diseases or to aid growth. The bantam breeder should be careful in using them since most antibiotics will result in bantams growing larger than normal.

ANTISEPTIC   A substance which retards or destroys bacterial growth. Any good proprietary brand should be used annually in connection with 'spring cleaning' operations and on chick rearing and other appliances when they are put away after use.

APERIENT   A substance with laxative properties which may be valuable under certain conditions. Epsom salts can be used when bantams are overfat. They should be penned on short rations and have the salts administered until they regain normal condition.

ASBESTOS   Non-inflammable material generally used in sheet form for the construction of bantam houses. Suitably framed it is vermin proof but has a tendency to coldness and condensation in winter unless proper ventilation is ensured.

ASHES   May be used, tightly rammed down, as basis for an earth floor e.g. in a scratching shed. Should not be used in the dust bath or scattered in the run as ashes tend to roughen bantams' legs and scaly leg soon follows.

ASPERGILLOSIS   A fungus disease usually affecting chicks between 2 and 6 weeks of age. Also known as 'Brooder Pneumonia'. Not very likely to be found in naturally reared chicks.

ASTRINGENT   A substance which dries up secretion from the skin. Useful property in a face lotion when getting bantams ready for show.

AVIAN TUBERCULOSIS   This is the 'going light' of old-time fanciers. If bantams are light in weight, with associated lameness and anaemia they should be killed and destroyed by burning.

AXIAL FEATHER   The small feather which separates primary from secondary wing feathers.

BACILLARY WHITE DIARRHOEA   B.W.D. can cause high mortality with few symptoms except the white discharge which results in pasted-up vents. All parent stock should be blood-tested and 'carriers' removed from the flock.

BAD EGG   It is possible for an egg to be held up in the oviduct and be bad when laid.

BALANCE   When a bantam is 'well balanced' it is symmetrical and all parts are in proportion.

BALANCED RATION Foods containing the proper ingredients for health, condition etc. Nowadays are usually prepared by large manufacturers, whose product is superior to home-mixed meals.

BALDNESS Results from several causes, chief of which are feather-picking, depluming mite, favus ('white face') or, in some cases, an over-vigorous cock continually harassing and mating his hens.

BALLING ON CHICKS' FEET Always keep a careful watch on chicks reared indoors, as they are liable to get meal or soil balling on their toes. Hard lumps should be well moistened and split so that they come away from the toe nails.

BARB The smaller shafts from the main quill of a feather.

BARBULES Extremely small hooked structures which join together the barbs.

BARLEY Not a particularly good grain for bantams, chiefly because it is rough and not very palatable. Wheat is preferred.

BEAK Of horn-like substance and divided into upper and lower mandibles, the nostrils being situated in the upper mandible.

BEARD Feathers growing under the throat of some bantams which originated on the Continent e.g. Polands.

BEEFY Term usually applied to the comb of a bantam considered for show or breeding. Denotes a thick, overgrown or coarse comb which is out of proportion.

BEETLE BROWS Overhanging brows would be a fault in all except a few breeds, notably Brahmas, Indian Game and Malays.

BICARBONATE OF SODA This well-known household commodity may be administered in solution to bantams which have digestive disorders.

BIOTIN Member of Vitamin B group. Necessary to prevent dermatitis in chicks. Deficiency not likely to occur in normal diet for bantams.

BISCUIT MEAL Good biscuit meal is sweet to the smell and taste and acceptable to bantams of all ages. Is rich in carbohydrates, low in fibre content and easily digested. Most used as a base for wet mash, when it should be soaked in cold water, then have surplus moisture squeezed out before being dried off with meal. Should not be given dry or will cause bantams to have crop disorders.

BLACK OR DARK COMB Can result from frostbite, liver disorder or general ill health. Isolate the bantam, determine cause and treat accordingly. Always safe to administer a mild aperient while under observation.

BLASTODERM The 'spot' seen on the yolk of an egg which may contain a germ. Does not necessarily indicate a fertile egg.

BLINDNESS Unless caused by a blow or other damage, any degree of blindness must be regarded with suspicion since it may be indicative of fowl paralysis or tapeworm infestation.

BLINKING   A bantam blinks by passing a third membrane across the eye and not by moving the upper or lower eyelid.

BLOCKY   Term used to denote a thick-set bantam, such as Indian Game.

BLOOD CYSTS   Bantams found to be bleeding profusely externally but show no evidence of direct injury may be suspected to suffer from blood cysts. Such bantams should not be left with the flock or used in the breeding pen.

BLOOD IN DROPPINGS   Red blood with brown, watery droppings may indicate worms; blood streaks may mean coccidiosis; dried, dull coloured blood may mean prolapsus.

BLOOD SPOTS   Found in eggs but do not affect their edible qualities. All eggs should be tested by candling and bantams habitually laying such eggs should not be included in the breeding pen.

BLOOM   On eggs or on bantams which have been properly prepared for exhibition. A term of praise.

BLUE MERCURIC OINTMENT   Used for scaly leg. After scrubbing with a nailbrush, carbolic soap and hot water legs are dried and the ointment applied with finger and thumb. Repeat weekly until masses come away. Then wash and dry, after which new scales will appear.

BODY LOUSE   Common form of lice on domestic poultry. Use insect powder, add powder to dust bath material or use perch paint based on nicotine sulphate.

BRACKEN   If gathered free in the country and stacked, makes useful winter litter after hard stalks have been taken out.

BRAN   Good, broad bran is floury and soft to the touch. Add up to 10% to wet mash if bantams are fat or laying soft-shelled eggs.

BRASSY   Yellow on top colour of males, chiefly Whites, which occurs only on the surface and should not be confused with sappiness.

BREED   All varieties of one sort of bantam bearing the same family name constitute a Breed.

BROKEN PLUMAGE   May be caused by exposure to weather, vigorous attention of the cock to the hens, depluming mites, lice or quill binding. Considerably lessens the chance of prizewinning at shows.

BRONCHITIS   A bantam which wheezes and gasps during the winter months may be overfat with some heart trouble. True bronchitis is difficult to cure and mortality rate is rapid and high.

BRONZE   A colour fault in self-black breeds which should have a rich, green sheen on their plumage.

BROODY COOP Appliance with wire or slatted floor in which broodies are placed to break them of the desire to sit, when they are not wanted for incubating eggs. It should be in full view of the other birds and food and water should be given in normal quantities.

BROWN A misnomer since 'Brown' bantams are actually a form of Black-red in plumage.

BRUSSELS SPROUTS Good winter greenfood. Surplus leaves should be shredded and fed from a trough. Main stems can be split lengthwise so that bantams may peck out the 'marrow'.

BUCKWHEAT May be added to grain ration, not exceeding 10% if cheapness warrants this action.

BUMBLEFOOT Likeliest to occur amongst very heavy breeds like Indian Game especially if their perches are set high. Soak foot in warm water to which disinfectant has been added. Lance the swelling and remove the 'corn' which has probably occurred, removing pus by pressure. Plug with cottonwool which has been soaked in disinfectant solution. Keep in pen, well littered with soft material until recovery.

CABBAGE Cabbage heart can be hung up for bantams to peck. All other leaves should be shredded before being fed to the birds.

CALCIUM Needed for general health and bone and shell formation. Limestone and shell grits supply sources of the mineral.

CALCIUM DEFICIENCY Reflected in soft-shelled eggs and leg weakness. In addition to supplying grit, dust mash with limestone flour until remedied.

CALCIUM OXIDE Is quicklime and should not be used to 'sweeten' runs unless applied in autumn and runs will be vacant for following 6 months of winter weather.

CANKER Shows as yellow, cheesy substance within the beak, Causes are coryza, fighting and fowl pox. *Treatment:* isolate sufferers, remove core and treat affected parts with iodine. Old fanciers often rub the places with a 'brimstone' (not safety) match head.

CAPE Feathers under the neck hackle and between the shoulders.

CAPSULE A small metal disc filled with alcohol used in incubators. Expansion and contraction regulates the temperature within the machine.

CARBOHYDRATE Starchy part of foods which must be balanced or fatness will ensue.

CARRIAGE General style and bearing of a bantam. Slight variation according to Standard requirements for different breeds.

CARROTS Useful winter 'greenfood' which should always be shredded and fed from a trough.

CASTOR OIL Half a teaspoonful for each bird when constipated or cropbound.

CELL In each cell is a nucleus which contains chromosomes. These determine the appearance and inherited factors of a bantam.

CHAFF Husks from corn, making ideal litter for bantam houses.

CHALAZAE On each side of the yolk of an egg is a thickened cord of albumen. While the egg is fresh these anchor the yolk in position.

CHAMOIS Alternative name for White-laced Buffs, as in Polands.

CHARACTERISTICS Points, laid down in Breed Standards, which define one breed from another. Varieties of one breed will share the same general characteristics.

CHICKEN When the term is met in show schedules, without further definition, it is usually interpreted as meaning bantams bred in the current year.

CHICKEN FEATHER Plumage worn before assuming adult feathers at about 5 months of age. Chicken feathers do not, usually, give a clear indication of what final colouring and markings will be.

CHICKWEED Common weed of the garden is excellent greenfood for chicks.

CHILLED EGGS A broody may leave her eggs, causing them to become chilled. If the hen returns or a new broody can be induced to sit on the eggs it ought to be worth while having them incubated for 22 days, as hatching may be delayed because of the chilling.

CHIPPED EGGS When chicks are ready to hatch, they chip their way round the broad dome of the egg. At this stage the broody should not be compelled to leave the nest for food or water.

CLASSIFICATION The whole of the classes set out in a show schedule.

CLEAR An infertile egg which shows up on testing at the seventh day.

CLIPPED OATS These have more feeding value than whole oats which are rather fibrous for most bantam breeds.

CLOACA Large portion at the end of the main intestine through which the egg comes and waste matter from the body passes.

CLOACITIS Commonly known as Vent Gleet. Shows as white discharge with offensive smell. *Treatment:* isolation, wash the parts with disinfectant solution and treat with penicillin cream.

CLOSE FEATHERING As in Old English Game and other hard-feathered breeds as opposed to the profusion required in some soft-feathered varieties.

CLUCKER (Northern, Clocker) Broody hen making the typical noise, indicative of a desire to sit on eggs.

COCCIDIOSIS Starts with loss of appetite, ruffled feathers, drooping wings and blood in droppings. Can soon prove fatal. Best treated by a proprietary medicine (usually, sulpha-group drugs). After attack is checked, houses, runs and all equipment should be thoroughly cleansed.

COCKLE SHELL GRIT Useful, along with other grits, and easily ingested by bantams.

COD LIVER OIL Rich in Vitamins A and D, is best incorporated in the wet mash and most useful for birds kept indoors in winter.

COMB PECKING Hens sometimes attack the comb of the male when in the breeding pen. Wounds should be dressed with Stockholm Tar, the affected bird being removed from the breeding pen and not returned until fully healed. He should be given nourishing food with extra greenstuff.

COMMON COLD Indicated by running nostrils. Check for house draughts. Wash headpoints with disinfectant solution, which also spray overhead when bantams are at roost.

CORNS Lame bantams should be examined for corns in the sole of the foot. These may be caused by bantams jumping on to a hard floor or by injury from a thorn or something similar. Gently remove corn and dress with tincture of iodine.

CORYZA Generally follows a common cold which has been neglected. Inflammation of the upper part of the respiratory tract is involved.

COVERTS There are both wing and tail coverts.

CRAMP Bantams on damp floors during winter months when they do not get enough exercise may be troubled with cramp. Provide warmer floor litter, freedom from draughts and plenty of greenfood with cod liver oil added to the mash.

CREOSOTE When this wood preservative is used inside a bantam house it should be applied at least a fortnight before the premises are wanted for use.

CREST Globular tuft of feathers growing from the top of the skull in breeds like Polands and Houdans.

CROOKED BACK Deformed condition marked by one side of the back being higher than the other. This renders the bantam useless for show or breeding.

CROOKED BREAST BONE The 'keel' is bent or dented. Not common under modern conditions. Any bantam so affected should not be used in the breeding pen. Severe inbreeding, lack of vitamins and use of narrow perches at an early age can cause the trouble.

CROOKED TOES Principally caused by close, careless inbreeding.

CROP BINDING Caused by indigestible food containing a lot of fibre, such as coarse greenfood or long, dry grass which has accumulated in the crop instead of passing down to the gizzard. Affected bantams should be penned alone and given a teaspoonful of olive oil, the crop being gently massaged. If not effective, a weak solution of bicarbonate of soda may be given through the beak, the crop massaged and emptied by holding the bantam head downwards while continuing to massage crop and neck. Give bread and milk until the sufferer has recovered.

CROP, SOUR Crop distended with evil smelling fluid. Treat with bicarbonate of soda, as for *Crop Binding*.

CROSSED BEAK Deformity in which the mandibles of the beak do not close correctly and the bantam has some difficulty in feeding. Should be a pointer to instant culling.

CROWING Usually taken as a sign of vigour in male bantams. There are no certain ways of stopping a healthy male from crowing, especially in the early morning.

CULL Reject from a stud by reason of colour, conformation etc.

CUSHION Part of a female bantam between the back and tail coverts.

DARI Corn, also known as sorghum. May be used in a grain mixture on same lines as buckwheat, q.v.

DAW Light colour of eyes, correct according to the Standard of some breeds, such as Malays.

DEAD IN SHELL Incubated eggs in which the embryo has died before being fully developed, Cause may be due to breeding methods, storage of eggs, feeding programme or fault in incubation.

DEPLUMING MITE These burrow under the skin near shafts of feathers causing them to break off leaving the bantam with unsightly red patches which may be scurfy. *Treatment:* clean house and burn all litter. Wash affected parts and dry. Apply carbolised Vaseline or carraway ointment. Recovery can be expected after moult.

DIAMOND Other name for wing bay or triangle at end of folded wing.

DISCOLOURED COMB May be due to several causes and cannot, in itself, denote any particular trouble. Some causes are liver trouble, heart disease, worms and frostbite.

DOWN First covering of baby chicks. This gives no guide to colour of adult plumage.

DRY MASH Prepared meals, fed as received from manufacturer. Should be contained in hoppers which are open during hours of daylight and accessible to the bantams but closed at night.

DUCK FOOTED When the back toe, instead of being in line with the middle toe, turns to one side, a bantam is said to be duck footed. Poor fertility will be experienced from birds so afflicted and they should be culled from the breeding pen.

DUST BATH   A box filled with fine sand or sieved, dry earth to which a little disinfectant powder has been added makes a good dust bath and helps bantams to rid themselves of insect pests.

EAR   Above the earlobe is the true ear, covered with small, hair-like feathers.

EGG BOUND   Bantam in lay is unable to pass an egg. Inbred bantams of small body size are likeliest to be affected. *Treatment:* hold bird over steaming hot water and smear vent gently with olive oil. Place bird in darkened pen with plenty of soft litter. Repeat as required until egg is passed.

EGG EATING   Generally starts by thin shelled eggs becoming broken. Culprits are discouraged if the upper mandible of their beak is filed so that they cannot 'jab' at eggs and break them.

ENLARGED CROP   Muscles and walls of crop have been stretched by overfeeding and the crop hangs like a pendulous bag. Spoils a bantam for showing but not for the breeding pen.

EPILEPSY   Spasms, gasping and convulsions all indicate epilepsy. Over-shown, fat males are likeliest to suffer. Keep in a shaded place on a light diet and give an aperient. Exclude from the breeding programme.

EPSOM SALTS   2 oz to a gallon of drinking water will suffice for general use, as an aperient for the flock.

EUCALYPTUS OIL   Useful for colds and nasal catarrh. Float a thin skin on the drinking water so that bantams get it round their nostrils when drinking or add it to a light pink solution of permanganate of potash for swabbing the nostrils of affected birds.

EXCESSIVE THIRST   Likely causes are worms or excessive salt in house scraps used in the mash.

EXTRA TOE   Some breeds, like Dorkings, have a fifth toe to accord with Standard requirements.

EYE DEFECTS   Unless known to be caused by accident, all sufferers should be kept out of the breeding pen.

FAVUS   Known for many years as 'white face'. Typical white or grey patches spread rapidly over the face. Treat with Vaseline to which has been added 5% Formalin or apply colourless vinegar and afterwards anoint with Vaseline.

FISH MEAL   Valuable animal protein which should not exceed 10% of the mash. Especially good for heavy layers or breeds with big development of feather.

FLIGHT FEATHERS   Ten long feathers are hidden when the wing is closed and are primaries. Bantams which habitually fly out of their runs can be restrained by cutting these feathers in one wing only.

FLINT GRIT Should be part of the contents of the grit trough. It helps to grind up food in the gizzard.

FLOWERS OF SULPHUR Old-fashioned remedy for body lice, used as a dusting powder or added to the dust bath.

FLUFF Soft, downy part of a feather seen in abundance in Pekins and similar breeds.

FOWL PEST A notifiable disease. No treatment should be given but everything about the plant should be disinfected and no visitors allowed. See full details in Chapter 18.

FRIARS BALSAM Can be applied to wounds to stop bleeding.

FROSTBITE Turns combs etc. a purplish colour, followed by blackening of the tips which may fall off. In frosty weather, apply Vaseline as a precaution.

FULLY FURNISHED Stage when all feathers are fully grown and accord to the Breed Standard.

FURNISHINGS All tail sickle and covert feathers and saddle hackles of male bantams.

GAPES Caused by a gapeworm affecting chicks up to 8 weeks of age. Individual cases may be treated by stripping a flight feather until it resembles a paint brush, dipping it in turpentine, inserting down the wind pipe, and then gently turning it round to remove the worms.

GAPING Not to be confused with gapes, this gaping affects adult stock and is usually a symptom of a disorder such as liver or heart disease or indigestion.

GIZZARD Function is to grind foods which have passed from the crop. Grit is used together with muscular action to effect this.

GRASS MEAL Add 5% to mash in winter to maintain yolk colour.

GREENFOOD Any cultivated crop or garden weed which is non-poisonous and free from chemical crop sprays may be used for bantams. Coarser leaves should be chopped and fed from a trough. Roots, such as Swedes, should be split and left for the birds to peck.

GRIZZLED Grey, generally in flights, of black or dark coloured bantams. Constitutes a fault.

GROUND COLOUR Basic colour in plumage to which markings are added.

HACKLES Long, narrow, pointed feathers on the necks of bantams. Similar feathers towards the tail of the male are saddle hackles.

HEAD LOUSE Often found on very young chicks which are being naturally reared. Dust broody hen with insect powder but a touch of olive oil on the louse and removing it with tweezers is only sure remedy.

HOT MASH Wet mash prepared with hot water and fed warm during winter months. The bucket can be stood on a stove for ten minutes before feeding to achieve even warmth.

HOUSE SCRAPS Should not exceed one quarter the total bulk of the mash and meat scraps and vegetable waste should be fairly evenly balanced. See that condiments are cleaned from plates before scraps are dropped into the food bucket.

IMPACTION OF PREEN GLAND The 'oil bottle' at the root of the tail becomes swollen and inflamed. Bathe with very warm water, pluck off the tiny hairs with tweezers, press gently and express oil. Bathe again with antiseptic and lightly smear with Vaseline. Repeat as required during next fortnight.

INCUBATION PERIOD Varying from 18 days for the small, old-time bantams to almost the full period of 21 days for recently made miniatures.

INSOLUBLE GRIT Flint or grey granite should be of the correct size and always available to the bantams. The softer grits do not serve the same purpose.

INTERNAL LAYER Visits the nest-box regularly and looks fit. Yolks are not passing into the oviduct but into the abdomen. Such bantams may pass tiny yolk-less eggs. *Treatment:* isolate, give a very light diet.

IRIS Coloured portion of the eye which varies according to Standard.

KAFFIR CORN Alternative name for dari or sorghum.

KALE Very useful greenfood for winter. Leaves should be shredded and fed from a trough, stems being split and impaled on a blunt nail.

KIDNEY DISEASE (Nephritis) Inflammation of the kidneys results in depression and discoloured face. Could be caused by badly balanced diet deficient in Vitamin A.

LACERATION (of the females) Wounds in the sides of hens caused by cocks with sharp, strong spurs. Such hens will give infertile eggs as they will resent mating. Remove from pen, isolate and treat wounds. Can be used for breeding when wounds completely healed. Shorten cock's spurs.

LAMENESS May be due to physical cause i.e. injury to pad by sharp stone or a symptom of disease such as paralysis.

LATENT Dormant, cannot be seen. A factor present in the make-up of a bantam which can be used to advantage. Contributory factor to the success of double-mating methods. See Chapter 15.

LEG WEAKNESS Likely to occur in early season when chicks are reared indoors. Vitamin deficiency may be cause. Cod liver oil and fresh greenfood are a big help but best safeguard is to use a proprietary chick rearing meal which is properly balanced.

LINSEED Traditional help to sheen and condition of plumage. Cover a handful of linseed (whole seed, not meal) with cold water and simmer in a pan on low heat. When cold the mass will be a jelly which can be incorporated in wet mash, three times weekly only.

LITTER Any non-poisonous trouble-free material would make suitable floor litter but recommendations are: wheat or oat chaff; peat moss; dried autumn leaves; cut straw; bracken; wood shavings from non-resinous woods; white sawdust.

LOBE BLISTERS Breeds, such as Rosecombs, often have blisters on the surface of their lobes. When required for show, such bantams should be shaded. Lobes should be washed and dried occasionally being finally dressed with violet powder. Blisters are caused by action of weather and small particles of grit adhering to them.

LUCERNE Greenfood which can be grown and fed fresh, being shredded and fed from a trough.

MAIZE Should be broken, cracked or kibbled for bantams. Can be added to grain ration for all except white plumaged birds in winter.

MANDIBLES Upper and lower horny parts of the beak.

MASH Mixture of meals for chicks, growers, breeders and layers. May be fed dry or moistened to form a 'wet' mash. Best used as issued by manufacturers.

MEDICINAL PARAFFIN Useful mild aperient, also for crop impaction.

MIDDLINGS The 'middle' of a grain of wheat between the outer bran and the inner kernel. Also known as thirds, boxings, wheatings and pollard. Middlings forms a rough flour which has a high carbohydrate content.

MILLET Small grain included in chick mixtures.

MUFF Feathers on each side of the face which help to form the furnishings of breeds like Belgian bantams.

NEST-BOX Should be well lined and in semi-darkness. Suitable for bantams is a box 12 in long, 9 in wide and 12 in high.

OLIVE OIL Suitable lubricant in cases of egg binding.

ONIONS Chopped finely, small amounts of raw onions can be fed to chicks from earliest stages. Provide natural sulphur, aiding feathering.

OYSTER SHELL Source of calcium in the grit box.

PAD Underpart of foot which, in certain breeds, aids identification of the true stock. White pads in Black Orpingtons are, for instance, a Standard requirement.

PALE SHANKS Yellow legged breeds often go pale in the shanks after a spell of heavy laying. Males should not be allowed latitude in this respect.

PALE YOLKS Generally result from insufficient raw greenfood or its equivalent. Grass meal and grated, raw carrots are both helpful.

PASTED-UP VENT (in chicks) Due to chills, irregular brooder heat or unbalanced diet. Bathe vent and apply a little oil. Watch for vent pecking and isolate if necessary.

PERCHES Best of 1½ in batten with top corners planed off.

PERCH PAINT Effective means of de-lousing bantams. Paint nicotine sulphate preparation on the perches before bantams go to roost.

POROUS SHELLS Flaky, chalky-looking eggs are unduly porous and should be excluded from those chosen for incubation.

PREENING Bantams rub their beaks against preen gland and apply oil to their feathers.

PRIMARY FEATHERS Ten wing feathers which are hidden when wing is normally closed.

PROTEIN FOODS Insects, worms etc. are natural protein. Fish and meat meals are prepared animal proteins. Peas, beans and nuts represent vegetable protein. All are valuable and necessary for development of sound plumage.

PULLET Generally refers to a female bantam during the first year of laying although, technically, she would be a hen after attaining maximum age of 14 months.

QUILL Hollow stem of fully developed feather.

QUILL BOUND As each new feather grows it pushes its way through a sheath which breaks to release it. When these sheaths fail to break, plumage is quill bound. Quill-bound feathers will be notched and marked when fully grown. Better feeding with more oil and protein is indicated, although weakly stock may often be so afflicted when stronger bantams are not; all being reared in the same way.

RED MITE Small, grey mite which become red when gorged with blood. Live in crevices of woodwork etc. Symptoms include pale faces and low vitality. Remedy, thorough cleansing of houses.

REVERSION Offspring revert to an ancestor and lack quality by present-day standards.

RICKETS Soft bones, enlarged joints and leg weakness are signs of this trouble. Cod liver oil and Vitamin D are needed in the mash, especially for winter chicks reared indoors.

ROACH BACK A 'hump' back resulting from defective spine.

SADDLE From middle of back to base of tail in male, feathers usually correspond to those in neck hackle.

SCALES Cover shanks and feet. After annual moult, when scales are renewed, the old scales can be removed with gentle pressure on their sides from thumb nail.

SCALY LEG   Roughness caused by a mite, resulting in typical chalky encrustations which result in lameness. See Blue Mercuric Ointment.

SECONDARIES   Outer wing feathers which can be seen when wings are normally closed.

SEPARATING THE SEXES   No hard-and-fast age for all breeds. Individual consideration should be given. Cockerels should not be left with pullets long enough to molest them.

SHAFT   Stem or quill portion of a feather.

SHANK   Part of leg between hock and toes.

SHEATH   Holds each new feather as it grows. Falls off naturally.

SHOULDER BUTTS   Ends of wings nearest the shoulders.

SHOULDERS   Front and upper part of wings.

SICKLES   Top pair of curved feathers in a male's tail.

SLATTED PLATFORM   Platform with solid sides about 4 in deep and slats set evenly along the top on which growers can perch before being transferred to larger houses.

SLIPPED WING   Primary feathers are out of natural order and can be seen when wing is normally closed.

SOFT-SHELLED EGGS   May be due to overfatness, heavy laying, lack of Vitamin D, or fright.

SPLIT WING   Wing with a gap between primary and secondary feathers. A serious fault and cause for rejection.

SPROUTED GRAIN   Useful to town bantam breeders for both breeding pens and chicks in winter season. Oats are soaked overnight, then spread on shallow boxes of peat moss which has been soaked and kept damp for a fortnight at about 70°F or in an airing cupboard. When sprouts are 2 to 3 in long, boxes are placed before the birds allowing 4 oz between six adults.

SPUR   Natural, horn-like growth on the inside of shanks, prominent in male bantams.

SPUR (removal of)   When cock's spurs are too long and sharp they should be removed in readiness for the breeding season or laceration of females will occur. Using a pad of soft cloth thoroughly soaked in cold water to protect the shank, the spur can be cut by heating an old dinner knife and using it with a sawing motion. The spur can thus be cut and the wound cauterised at the same time.

SQUIRREL TAIL   Tail projects forwards over the back instead of at the normal angle laid down by Breed Standards.

STANDARD OF PERFECTION   Points for all breeds total 100 for the perfect bird. They are detailed by Breed Clubs and approved by The Poultry Club and British Bantam Association. The book, *British Poultry Standards,* gives them fully.

SULPHATE OF IRON   Dissolve 1 oz in a pint of water and use as a stock solution for tonic purposes. Rate is one tablespoonful of the solution to half a gallon of drinking water, using non-metal vessels.

TAIL   Fourteen stiff tail feathers, seven on each side, constitute the tail of a bantam.

TASSEL   Allowable in Old English Game where feathers form a topknot which is not full and circular like a crest but more in the nature of a skylark's topping.

THIGH   Upper portion of leg, above shank.

TURPENTINE   Used for attacks of gapes in chicks. See Gapes.

TYPE   Body shape, carriage and allied characteristics are known as 'type' and distinguish one breed from another.

UPPER WEB   Many Breed Standards give definitions of colour and markings which may vary between the upper and lower webs of wing feathers.

VERTIGO   Dizziness, causing a bantam to stagger and collapse. *Treatment:* isolation in cool, sheltered place. Mild aperient and light diet to be given.

VITALITY   Health and vigour, inherited from parents, should be a point of selection in all breeding stock. It can be ruined by bad feeding and careless management.

WATERY DROPPINGS   Indigestion, worms and excitement may be contributory factors.

WATTLES   Folds of skin, of specific shape and colour, hang from the underside of the beak.

WEB   Of feather, flat plumage on either side of the shaft; also used for skin between the toes.

WHISKERS   Feathers growing from the sides of the face in muffed breeds.

WING BAR   Bar of feathers across middle of wing best seen in Black-red coloured breeds.

WING BAY   Triangular part at end of the normally closed wing.

WING BOW   The shoulder of the wing.

WING BUTT   The upper 'corner' of the wing.

WING COVERTS   Feathers which cover roots of secondary quills.

WIRE NETTING   Excellent for closed runs. 1 in mesh is a good size as it keeps bantams' heads within the run and many wild birds out.

WRY TAIL   Carried to one side, permanently. A fault which should result in complete rejection for either show or breeding.

INDEX